Acknowledgements

A big thanks to all those who worked so hard (and so fast!) on this project…
Writing/research team: Bob Moog, Jeff Pinsker, Erin Conley, Rosie Slattery, and Christine Brenneman.
Editing team: Bob Moog, Jeff Pinsker, Erin Conley, Rosie Slattery, and Jenny Brennan.
Proofing/fact-checking team: Heather Russell, Jenny Brennan, Suzanne Cracraft,
Susan King, and Erin Conley.
Design/production team: Michael Friedman, Jeff Batzli, Rick Campbell, and Richela Morgan.
Sales and promotions team: Michael Friedman, Bruce Lubin, Mary Carlomagno, and Jules Herbert.
A special thanks to the following UG staffers for their brain-power: Jene Aguilar, Marlon Andaya,
Francesca Araneta, Amy Aves, Jenny Brennan, Al Calmerin, Diane Carlson, John Cervelli, Jennifer Cho,
Tom Cracraft, Lynette Cravens, John DeBenidictus, Dawn Dobrovich, Minh Du, Tatiana Emelianova,
Mik Gaspay, Tyler Glenn, Teresa Goodbody, Sheila Harvey, Audrey Haworth, Alexis Herrera, Norm Hicks,
Joyce Hirohata, Moss Kardener, Katesha Kennebrew, Megan Kilian, Anthony King, Susan King,
Vince Kurr, Michelle Lee, Claudia Lee-Escobar, Betty Lim, Mike Lynch, Igor Mederios, Andy Moberg,
Curtis Monlin, Todd Mullins, David Norman, Jennifer Pack, Steve Peek, Evelyn Salguero,
Jose Santiago, Jim Stern, Cory Storm, Melissa Torok, Derick Tullis, Kenneth Vanbenberg,
Jim Yan, and Claude Zamaripa.
Original concept includes Steve Morris of IQ 2000 Products.
We couldn't have done it without your knowledge and know-how!

ISBN 1-57528-901-6

Printed in Mexico

01 02 03 04 MC 9 8 7 6 5 4 3 2 1

Table of Contents

Introduction

Cris Lehman and I weren't kidding when we started University Games on April Fool's Day in 1985. Our goal was serious: to design and develop a new type of board game. We wanted to combine fun and education, and to create a game where people of different backgrounds and different knowledge bases could play together.

When our friend, Steve Morris, introduced us to his game IQ 2000, we knew right away that this was the concept we'd been looking for. Jeff Pinsker, our ace game developer, and I suggested marketing it under its European name, Game of Knowledge—and an instant winner was born. As you read the book and play the game, you'll notice that *Game of Knowledge* is not a typical trivia game. Notice how carefully each question is crafted to help you come up with the correct answer. Our hope is that as you play along, you'll be surprised by what you do know, rather than what you don't.

Here's to a good game!

Bob

Rules

How It Works
While many games challenge your memory of obscure facts, Game of Knowledge gauges how much attention you pay to the world around you. The game features hundreds (and hundreds!) of questions based on knowledge drawn from—and relevant to—everyday life.

So, as you play, listen carefully…Many questions provide hints or clues to help you draw on your knowledge and jump-start your brain! You may be impressed at how much you already know—and how much you can learn from the Game of Knowledge.

Object
Be the first player to win one point in each topic, or collect 10 points all together.

The Way to Play
First things first: grab a pen and paper to keep track of your points.

The youngest player spins first and is the Reader for the first round of play. The Reader now flips to the first block of questions in the book and reads a question from the topic spun (i.e. Fame, Nature, Media, Our World, Sports, or Science) to the player on his/her left.

If the player guesses correctly, s/he receives a point for that topic.

If the player guesses incorrectly, play continues in a clockwise direction, with the Reader reading the next player the next question in the block. (For example, if the first player gets Media, the second player gets Our World, the third gets Sports, and so on…Got it? Good!). There is no penalty for an incorrect response.

After all players have answered a question, the person to the Reader's left takes a spin and is now the Reader for the next block of questions.

Winning the Game
The first player to win one point in each topic, or to collect 10 points all together, is the winner!

Playing On Your Own
Spin, flip to the first page of the round, and read the topic question from the appropriate section. Don't forget to keep the answer covered with a bookmark.

If you guess correctly, give yourself a point and spin again. If you guess incorrectly, take away a point. If you have no points, simply continue playing.

Collect six points in twenty minutes or less and you're a winner!

Round 1

BLOCK 1

FAME
Q: What actor/politician played a leading role in *Star Wars*, but never worked with George Lucas?
A: Ronald Reagan

NATURE
Q: Name the American Beauties prized for their hips.
A: Roses

MEDIA
Q: What chip off the old block's animated birth was one of the most popular TV episodes of the 1960s?
A: Pebbles Flintstone

OUR WORLD
Q: Which English philosopher was influential in early American political thought and has a name that begs you to stick a key into it?
A: John Locke

SPORTS
Q: What rotund president is often credited with creating the "Seventh Inning Stretch" in 1910?
A: President Taft

SCIENCE
Q: What natural material can turn into a diamond and was often used for copying in the days before the photocopier was an office staple?
A: Carbon

• •

SCIENCE
Q: True or false? Some dinosaurs were as small as chickens are today.
A: True

SPORTS
Q: Which St. Louis Cardinal shares his nickname with a McDonald's sandwich?
A: Mark McGwire (Big Mac)

OUR WORLD
Q: What can you always find surrounding an archipelago?
A: Water (An archipelago is a group of islands.)

MEDIA
Q: What royal color appears in the title of Alice Walker's most famous book?
A: Purple (*The Color Purple*)

NATURE
Q: What eerily named valley is the lowest point in the North American continent?
A: Death Valley, CA

FAME
Q: What Nobel Peace Prize winner died the same week as Princess Diana and was known for founding the Kalighat Home for the Dying?
A: Mother Theresa

BLOCK 2

BLOCK 3

FAME

Q: One of Nicolas Cage's first flicks was a love story about a downtown punk and the girl from a Los Angeles suburb he, like, totally fell for. What was it?
A: *Valley Girl*

NATURE

Q: Linen and linseed oil both originate from what plant?
A: Flax

MEDIA

Q: Which 1997 movie won multiple Academy Awards®—despite its "sinking" plot?
A: *Titanic*

OUR WORLD

Q: Louis XIV's nickname centers around what celestial body?
A: The sun (The Sun King)

SPORTS

Q: Which of these is hockey star Mario Lemieux's nickname: Nintendo Man, Super Mario, or Lemazing?
A: Super Mario

SCIENCE

Q: Which of these rock groups shares its name with the inventor of the seed drill: Jethro Tull, Pink Floyd, or Dr. Feelgood?
A: Jethro Tull

SCIENCE

Q: What endangered bird is often spotted in debates between loggers and conservationists in the Pacific Northwest?
A: The spotted owl

SPORTS

Q: In the 1980s the Atlanta Falcons' Head Coach, Jerry Glanville, had will-call tickets to every home game reserved for what deceased rockstar?
A: Elvis Presley

OUR WORLD

Q: As of March 2001, which U.S. presidents are not buried in the U.S.?
A: The ones that are still living! (Ford, Carter, Reagan, Bush, Clinton, Bush)

MEDIA

Q: In what mountainous country did the alpenhorn originate?
A: Switzerland

NATURE

Q: Bear this in mind: do you know what to call the young of a shark?
A: A cub

FAME

Q: What "small" story made Louisa May Alcott a big success?
A: *Little Women*

BLOCK 4

GAME OF KNOWLEDGE

FAME
Q: The savage pirate Edward Teach is better known by the color of his facial hair. What name did he go by?
A: Blackbeard

NATURE
Q. The largest of the Great Lakes lives up to its name. Name the lake.
A: Lake Superior

MEDIA
Q: What psychedelic flower caused Dorothy and her friends to fall asleep on the way to Oz?
A: Poppies

OUR WORLD
Q: To buy sushi in Tokyo, what will you need?
A: Yen

SPORTS
Q: In baseball, what does ERA stand for?
A: Earned Run Average

SCIENCE
Q: Name the bright nineteenth century inventor who holds the record for the most patents in history.
A: Thomas Alva Edison

SCIENCE
Q: In 1957, the USSR sent a loyal 11-pound mammal named Laika into orbit. What kind of animal was Laika?
A: A dog

SPORTS
Q: Ross Rebagliati took home a Gold in the 1998 Olympic debut of what cool sport?
A: Snowboarding

OUR WORLD
Q: Name two of the three U.S. states with four-letter names.
A: Iowa, Ohio, or Utah

MEDIA
Q: What Chicago-based rock group is named after a mean-spirited Halloween prank?
A: Smashing Pumpkins

NATURE
Q: What statuesque mammal gives birth standing up, often welcoming its offspring into the world with a six-foot plunge to the ground?
A: Giraffes

FAME
Q: What food expert sports an English accent even though she was born in Pasadena, CA?
A: Julia Child

BLOCK 7

FAME
Q: What was the long-held secret to Samson's supernatural strength?
A: His hair

NATURE
Q: As a percentage of total body length, roughly how long does a swordfish's sword grow to be: 10%, 30% or 50%?
A: 30%

MEDIA
Q: Which 1970s sex symbol got serious in *Extremities* and *The Burning Bed*?
A: Farrah Fawcett

OUR WORLD
Q: How many turtles go into one quart of mock turtle soup?
A: None

SPORTS
Q: While the Major League World Series is played in both teams' hometowns, what "little" event is held each year in Williamsburg, PA?
A: The Little League Baseball World Series

SCIENCE
Q: Which U.S. state consumes the most energy per person?
A: Alaska

- -

SCIENCE
Q: Which element shares its name with a high-tech valley in California and is the most abundant on Earth after oxygen?
A: Silicon

SPORTS
Q: What figure skating star had a signature haircut that became all the rage in the 1970s?
A: Dorothy Hamill

OUR WORLD
Q: The three most popular modes of worldwide transportation also share their names with a Steve Martin movie. What are they?
A: Planes, trains and automobiles

MEDIA
Q: Name two of the working costumes worn by members of The Village People.
A: Cowboy, police officer, construction worker, Indian

NATURE
Q: What aquatic grass plays an essential role in any symphony orchestra?
A: Reed

FAME
Q: What royal family rules Britain and has a castle bearing their name?
A: The Windsors

BLOCK 8

BLOCK 9

FAME
Q: Which controversial president shares his middle name with Bart Simpson's best friend?
A: Richard "Milhous" Nixon

NATURE
Q: This cave dweller is the only mammal that can fly. Name it.
A: The bat

MEDIA
Q: What was Anthony Edwards's fine-feathered nickname in the movie *Top Gun*?
A: Goose

OUR WORLD
Q: What Himalayan mountain has received international media attention for the adventurers who have unwittingly died there?
A: Mount Everest

SPORTS
Q: What famous pitcher first distinguished himself in the Negro League and is the oldest player to appear in a Major League Baseball game at 59 years old?
A: Satchel Paige

SCIENCE
Q: What theory "drifted" into the mind of Alfred Wegener in the early 1900s about the placement of the seven continents on the globe?
A: The continental drift theory

• •

SCIENCE
Q: Surf's up! Is a long, unbroken series of waves called a trough, a crest, or a swell?
A: A swell

SPORTS
Q: Name two of the four swimming strokes that make up the individual medley.
A: Butterfly, backstroke, breaststroke, or freestyle

OUR WORLD
Q: What direction do you screw in a light bulb: clockwise or counterclockwise?
A: Clockwise

MEDIA
Q: What mega-menace does Sheriff Brody set out to kill in a classic 1975 flick?
A: A great white shark (*Jaws*)

NATURE
Q: What natural wonder is comprised of Horseshoe Falls and American Falls?
A: Niagara Falls

FAME
Q: What professional athlete hit 361 home runs and scored with Marilyn Monroe?
A: Joe DiMaggio

BLOCK 10

BLOCK 11

FAME
Q: What city is both the capital of Illinois and Bart Simpson's hometown?
A: Springfield

NATURE
Q: True or false? Many snakes use their tongues to smell.
A: True

MEDIA
Q: As of 2001, how many *Rocky* movies are there?
A: Five

OUR WORLD
Q: What tangy blue cheese is named for a little town in France?
A: Roquefort (Roquefort-Sur-Soulzon)

SPORTS
Q: What occurs every four years and is the most watched sporting event on Earth?
A: The World Cup (Soccer)

SCIENCE
Q: Who was the first American woman to ride into space?
A: Sally Ride

- -

SCIENCE
Q: Which chemical element, whose symbol is the letter "C," is used to determine age?
A: Carbon

SPORTS
Q: Name four of the five NFL teams that are named after birds.
A: Falcons, Ravens, Cardinals, Seahawks, or Eagles

OUR WORLD
Q: Which is the shortest: the St. Louis Arch, the Eiffel Tower, or the Washington Monument?
A: The Washington Monument (555 feet)

MEDIA
Q: In George Selden's book, what melodious, nocturnal insect lives in Times Square?
A: A cricket (*A Cricket in Times Square*)

NATURE
Q: What plant's thick, aromatic root flavors Chinese dishes, soda pop, and "snaps"?
A: Ginger

FAME
Q: What English rocker set down roots and sang lead for Led Zeppelin?
A: Robert Plant

BLOCK 12

FAME
Q: Name the French President whose last name sounds like he had a lot of nerve.
A: Charles de Gaulle

NATURE
Q: What furry tree-dweller gets its name from an Australian Aboriginal word that means "no drink animal"?
A: Koala

MEDIA
Q: What TV show were the Beastie Boys referring to when they sang, "It's like Sam the butcher bringing Alice the meat … "?
A: *The Brady Bunch*

OUR WORLD
Q: What colorful name belongs to the modern-day land where Erik the Red established a Viking colony in the tenth century?
A: Greenland

SPORTS
Q: What appendage of basketball player Bob Lanier's body was the largest in professional sports during his career?
A: His feet—an amazing size 22

SCIENCE
Q: What vaccine did medical scientist Jonas Salk perfect in 1952?
A: The polio vaccine

- -

SCIENCE
Q: What critical innovation did Kirkpatrick Macmillan add to the bicycle in 1839 that made riding uphill a whole lot easier?
A: Pedals!

SPORTS
Q: In soccer, what is the name of the player who plays both offense and defense and is in the middle of the line up?
A: Half back

OUR WORLD
Q: How's it going? My name's Richard, but you can call me…What are the four most common nicknames for Richard?
A: Rick, Dick, Rich, and Ricky

MEDIA
Q: Who was the shyest dwarf in *Snow White and the Seven Dwarfs*?
A: Bashful

NATURE
Q: What club, named for a California mountain range, is the U.S.'s leading grassroots conservation organization?
A: The Sierra Club

FAME
Q: Name the bouncing, striped animal that lives in The 100-acre Wood.
A: Tigger

BLOCK 15

FAME
Q: Name the fresh prince who had an early hit with "Parents Just Don't Understand."
A: Will Smith

NATURE
Q: True or false? Quicksand has no suction power and contains enough water so that the human body can float on it.
A: True

MEDIA
Q: According to the Book of Genesis, God says: "Let there be…" what?
A: Light

OUR WORLD
Q: What Chinese dialect shares its name with a small orange?
A: Mandarin

SPORTS
Q: 42 is the only number you will never see on a Major League baseball uniform. This is a gesture of respect for whom?
A: Jackie Robinson

SCIENCE
Q: Which of these nutrients does your body need the least: fats, protein, or carbohydrates?
A: Fats

• •

SCIENCE
Q: According to Copernicus, who repudiated the Ptolemic theory, what is at the center of the universe?
A: The sun (not Earth)

SPORTS
Q: What Ohio city shares its name with a province in China and is home to the Football Hall of Fame?
A: Canton

OUR WORLD
Q: What Pacific Northwest city is named for the Greek home of the gods?
A: Olympia, Washington

MEDIA
Q: What controversial rapper's real name is Marshall Mathers?
A: Eminem

NATURE
Q: What prized fur-bearing rodent lives in the Andes mountains and takes its baths in volcanic dust rather than water?
A: Chinchilla

FAME
Q: Between 1992 and 2001 what actor showed up in Philadelphia, in the South, and on a tropical island?
A: Tom Hanks

BLOCK 16

BLOCK 17

FAME
Q: What hero of the scientific world said that, relatively speaking, light always traveled at a constant speed?
A: Albert Einstein

NATURE
Q: What African nation is also the fourth largest island in the world?
A: Madagascar

MEDIA
Q: Which two *Peanuts* characters had a crush on Charlie Brown?
A: Peppermint Patty and Marcy

OUR WORLD
Q: Which female teenage crusader heard God's calling and was burned at the stake?
A: Joan of Arc

SPORTS
Q: Strong-minded Craig MacTavish was the last hockey player to play the game without what?
A: A helmet

SCIENCE
Q: Which of these elements provides the fissionable material for nuclear bombs: palladium, platinum, or plutonium?
A: Plutonium

SCIENCE
Q: Linus Pauling won two Nobel Prizes and hoped to win a third for his work with what vitamin?
A: Vitamin C

SPORTS
Q: Which ancient city held the first modern Olympics in 1896: New York, Athens, or Madrid?
A: Athens

OUR WORLD
Q: In what twentieth century decade was the first African-American elected governor of a U.S. state?
A: The 1990s (1990, L. Douglas Wilder, Virginia)

MEDIA
Q: In what spot do Tom Hanks and Meg Ryan have their highly anticipated meeting in *Sleepless in Seattle?*
A: On top of the Empire State Building

NATURE
Q: What African river-dwelling mammal's lips are about two feet wide?
A: Hippopotamus

FAME
Q: What nineteenth century author, famous for his eerie stories, wrote the words "Quoth the Raven, 'Nevermore'"?
A: Edgar Allan Poe

BLOCK 18

BLOCK 19

FAME
Q: What national monument features four heads of state and was a blast to make?
A: Mount Rushmore

NATURE
Q: What green herb gives many pickles their distinctive taste?
A: Dill

MEDIA
Q: What U.S. president-to-be wrote *Profiles in Courage* and was also the youngest man to be elected to the office?
A: John F. Kennedy

OUR WORLD
Q: During World War II, Britain bested Germany in the Battle of Britain. Was this battle fought on land, sea, or air?
A: Air

SPORTS
Q: In football, numbers 1 through 19 are usually reserved for which two types of players?
A: Quarterbacks and kickers

SCIENCE
Q: Name the place on earth where tomorrow becomes today.
A: The International Date Line

• •

SCIENCE
Q: Which of these animals is not a mollusk: an octopus, an oyster, or a shark?
A: A shark

SPORTS
Q: Where was the first "lawn tennis" world championship held?
A: Wimbledon, England

OUR WORLD
Q: The Red Cross' flag (red cross against white) is the opposite of the flag of the country where it was founded. Name the country.
A: Switzerland

MEDIA
Q: According to the title of Cole Porter's 1934 musical, what goes?
A: Anything (*Anything Goes*)

NATURE
Q: What regal insects are found fluttering in the natural habitat of their favorite food, milkweed?
A: Monarch butterflies

FAME
Q: Hayley Mills played twin sisters of divorced parents in the original version of what 1960s Disney film?
A: *The Parent Trap*

BLOCK 20

• **16** •

BLOCK 21

FAME
Q: What four plastic body parts were made to stick in the first Mr. Potato Head®?
A: Eyes, ears, nose, and mouth

NATURE
Q: True or false? Porcupines fight their predators by shooting quills at them.
A: False (They swing their tails.)

MEDIA
Q: How many castaways were stranded on *Gilligan's Island*?
A: Seven

OUR WORLD
Q: Historically, have women's shirts had buttons on the left side or the right side?
A: The left side

SPORTS
Q: What new gymnastics event sprung up in the 2000 Olympics in Sydney?
A: The trampoline

SCIENCE
Q: It takes Venus 225 days to orbit the sun and Mars 687 days. How many days does it take Earth to orbit the sun?
A: 365 days

• •

SCIENCE
Q: True or false? If one part of a parallel circuit is broken, the circuit continues to function.
A: True

SPORTS
Q: What is the largest possible number of points on a single play in NBA basketball?
A: Four (a three-point shot plus a free throw)

OUR WORLD
Q: What two far-flung states were the last added to the Union in 1959?
A: Alaska and Hawaii

MEDIA
Q: Before he became an actor, Jason Lee (*Almost Famous*, *Chasing Amy*, and *Mall Rats*) was a professional in which sport: tennis, skateboarding, or soccer?
A: Skateboarding

NATURE
Q: In the Pacific they're called typhoons, but what are traveling tropical cyclones called when they occur in the Atlantic?
A: Hurricanes

FAME
Q: What heavy metal rock bands emblazon the shirts of Beavis and Butthead?
A: AC/DC and Metallica

BLOCK 22

BLOCK 23

FAME
Q: In what movie do Richard Dreyfuss, Ron Howard, and Harrison Ford meet at Mel's Drive-In?
A: *American Graffiti*

NATURE
Q: It's no joke: these cunning sub-Saharan hunters live in clans run by females. Name them.
A: Hyenas

MEDIA
Q: What limitless destination does Buzz Lightyear declare before he "flies" in *Toy Story*?
A: "To infinity and beyond"

OUR WORLD
Q: What country, later a Cold War enemy of the U.S., unloaded Alaska in an 1867 transaction known as Seward's Folly?
A: Russia

SPORTS
Q: True or false? The Cleveland Browns are named after the Brown Bear.
A: False (They're named for the legendary coach Paul Brown)

SCIENCE
Q: Which of the following is an organ that spiders use to spin silk threads for their webs: spinning tube, spinneret, or ganglion?
A: Spinneret

SCIENCE
Q: Italian mathematician and astronomer Galileo Galilei illuminated us by discovering that the moon is visible because it reflects light from what star?
A: The sun

SPORTS
Q: In the U.S., which is higher: the number of kids who play American Youth Soccer Organization soccer or the number who play Little League baseball?
A: Kids who play American Youth Soccer

OUR WORLD
Q: Which "cheesy" state touches Lake Michigan?
A: Wisconsin

MEDIA
Q: Name the U.S. state that provides the nickname for the main characters in John Steinbeck's depression-era epic, *The Grapes of Wrath*?
A: Oklahoma (Okies)

NATURE
Q: Which green herb often appears on plates in many restaurants because it removes garlic from the breath?
A: Parsley

FAME
Q: What two-term vice president (and long-time presidential hopeful) hails from the same state as Davy Crockett?
A: Al Gore

BLOCK 24

BLOCK 25

FAME	Q: What television twosome took a shot at dating in college only to find out that they really weren't meant for each other (since he's gay). A: Will and Grace
NATURE	Q: Which uni-horned pachyderm has a prehensile lip that acts similarly to a finger, selecting preferred foods for snacking? A: Rhinoceros
MEDIA	Q: Which eighteenth century Austrian composer is the subject of the film *Amadeus*? A: Wolfgang Amadeus Mozart
OUR WORLD	Q: What flavor pie is America's favorite? A: Apple
SPORTS	Q: On what holiday weekend is the Indianapolis 500 held? A: Memorial Day
SCIENCE	Q: Does a reflecting telescope gather light with a lens or a mirror? A: A mirror

SCIENCE	Q: Which of the following—the heart, the lungs, or the kidneys—have been successfully transplanted from one human to another? A: All three
SPORTS	Q: True or false? In volleyball, your team will always score a point if the other team fails to return the ball. A: False (only if your team served)
OUR WORLD	Q: True or false? Portland, Oregon is farther north than Portland, Maine. A: True
MEDIA	Q: In tic-tac-toe, what is the feline-sounding name for a game where neither side wins? A: A cat's game
NATURE	Q: Name two of the four longest rivers in the world. A: Nile, Amazon, Chang Jiang, and Mississippi
FAME	Q: Which of these artists painted the ceiling of the Sistine Chapel: Da Vinci, Michelangelo, or Raphael? A: Michelangelo

BLOCK 26

BLOCK 27

FAME
Q: What actress helped the medicine go down in *Mary Poppins*?
A: Julie Andrews

NATURE
Q: What is the masculine-sounding name of the island in the Irish Sea that is home to the tailless Manx cat?
A: The Isle of Man

MEDIA
Q: What gleeful actor played bus driver Ralph Kramden on *The Honeymooners*?
A: Jackie Gleason

OUR WORLD
Q: What British dependency is located entirely on a huge limestone rock?
A: Gibraltar

SPORTS
Q: In 1885, the Cuban Giants became the first organized group of what kind of baseball professionals?
A: African-American players

SCIENCE
Q: When wind or water wears away land over time, is it called erosion, emulsion, or eruption?
A: Erosion

- -

SCIENCE
Q: True or false? Applying force to an object causes acceleration in the direction of the force.
A: True

SPORTS
Q: Which player won a career Grand Slam in 1999 and had a perfect match with Steffi Graf?
A: Andre Agassi

OUR WORLD
Q: Which "Father of the Constitution" was married to a famous cook and hostess?
A: James Madison (married to Dolly Madison)

MEDIA
Q: Which *Rugrats* character sounds like an angel but bullies the babies?
A: Angelica

NATURE
Q: What type of fungus usually has a cap and gills?
A: The mushroom

FAME
Q: Who was the first Gandhi to become Prime Minister of India: Mahatma, Indira, or Rajiv?
A: Indira (1966)

BLOCK 28

BLOCK 29

FAME
Q: According to Greek legend, who stole fire from the gods and gave it to humans: Zeus, Neptune, or Prometheus?
A: Prometheus

NATURE
Q: True or false? An ostrich's eye is bigger than its brain.
A: True

MEDIA
Q: Some say that the "World's Greatest Rock and Roll Band" gathers no moss. Name the group's lead singer.
A: Mick Jagger of the Rolling Stones

OUR WORLD
Q: Name the Arabian prophet who founded the Muslim religion.
A: Mohammed

SPORTS
Q: What sailing term shares its name with a bulletin board item?
A: Tack

SCIENCE
Q: What solid matter do the words igneous, sedimentary, and metamorphic describe?
A: Rocks

• •

SCIENCE
Q: Which of these animals brought the bubonic plague from Europe to Asia in the fourteenth century: horses, goats, or rats?
A: Rats

SPORTS
Q: In golf, which club is generally used to hit the ball farther: a five iron, a seven iron, or a nine iron?
A: A five iron

OUR WORLD
Q: What Creole-cooking state borders Mississippi?
A: Louisiana

MEDIA
Q: What actress played an assistant newsroom producer on a top-rated TV show in the 1970s?
A: Mary Tyler Moore

NATURE
Q: What type of mountain gets its name from the Roman God of Fire?
A: The volcano (Vulcan)

FAME
Q: The TV series *Lost in Space* featured Robbie—a walking, talking what?
A: Robot

BLOCK 30

BLOCK 31

FAME
Q: What Hollywood heartthrob married a friend in 2000?
A: Brad Pitt (married Jennifer Aniston)

NATURE
Q: If visibility is over about 3,000 feet, you can call it mist or haze, but if you can't see within 3,000 feet it's called what?
A: Fog

MEDIA
Q: What famous Joker also flew over the cuckoo's nest?
A: Jack Nicholson

OUR WORLD
Q: What Asian desert actually boasts high mountains and springs, steep lands, and a rich animal kingdom?
A: Gobi

SPORTS
Q: In a surprising disappointment, what nation did not medal in any gymnastics events (men's or women's) in the 2000 Olympics?
A: The U.S.

SCIENCE
Q: Rachel Carson's 1962 book *Silent Spring* made people look more carefully at what they were eating. What did it describe the dangers of?
A: Pesticides (such as DDT and other chlorinated hydrocarbons)

SCIENCE
Q: In the animal kingdom, which is larger: a family, a genus, or a species?
A: A family

SPORTS
Q: In 1982, Michael Jordan led which southern school to the NCAA basketball title: North Carolina, North Carolina State, or Duke?
A: North Carolina

OUR WORLD
Q: Two twentieth century U.S. presidents from different political parties share a last name. What is the name?
A: Roosevelt (Theodore and Franklin)

MEDIA
Q: Name the young detective whose first name is a reference book and whose last name is a color.
A: Encyclopedia Brown

NATURE
Q: True or false? Camels are omnivores, feasting on plants, honey, and insects.
A: False. (Camels are vegetarians.)

FAME
Q: In Simon and Garfunkel's song "The Sound of Silence," what does the deadly silence grow like?
A: Cancer

BLOCK 32

BLOCK 33

FAME
Q: Which U.S. president tried to restore the nation's confidence in a government tarnished by scandal during his brief two and a half years in office?
A: Gerald Ford

NATURE
Q: The worst drought in North American history took place during what decade?
A: The 1930s (The Dustbowl)

MEDIA
Q: What type of animal leapt to fame in Mark Twain's story about Calaveras County, California?
A: A frog

OUR WORLD
Q: What western state, home to lots of cowboys, became the first U.S. state to allow women to vote in 1890?
A: Wyoming

SPORTS
Q: What is the colorful name for a college player who is kept out of competition for a year?
A: Redshirt

SCIENCE
Q: Which planet's name comes first in the alphabet?
A: Earth

• •

SCIENCE
Q: Which of these branches of science deals with matter and energy, and their relationship: biology, zoology, or physics?
A: Physics

SPORTS
Q: What comical sports team set an attendance record for their sport at Olympic Stadium in West Berlin?
A: The Harlem Globetrotters (for basketball)

OUR WORLD
Q: What Southeast Asian country, known for its Pad, was formerly called the kingdom of Siam?
A: Thailand

MEDIA
Q: The earliest known musical instruments (roughly 30,000 years old) were bones pierced with holes. Name the instrument.
A: Whistle or flute

NATURE
Q: How many different colors appear in a rainbow: 7, 8, or 9?
A: 7

FAME
Q: What acclaimed director also writes, acts, and plays the clarinet?
A: Woody Allen

BLOCK 34

BLOCK 35

FAME
Q: What are the first and last names of the lucky boy who inherits Willy Wonka's chocolate factory?
A: Charlie Bucket

NATURE
Q: Name the seed of a tropical tree that is big and brown and often sold in grocery stores.
A: Coconut (Palm tree)

MEDIA
Q: Is the TV character Lassie a male dog or a female dog?
A: A female dog

OUR WORLD
Q: Which country is the top wine-drinking nation in the world, based on liters per capita?
A: France

SPORTS
Q: What happened to the Brooklyn Dodgers, the New York Giants, and the St. Louis Browns in the 1950s?
A: They all moved to new cities.

SCIENCE
Q: What natural disaster's magnitude does the Richter Scale measure?
A: An earthquake

SCIENCE
Q: Who was the first person in space: Yuri Gagarin, John Glenn, or Alan Shepard?
A: Yuri Gagarin

SPORTS
Q: Which popular sport is closest to rugby: baseball, football, or lacrosse?
A: Football

OUR WORLD
Q: True or false? The idea that the means justify the end is the primary concept in Machiavelli's *The Prince*.
A: False (Just the opposite—the end justifies the means)

MEDIA
Q: What type of animal lends its name to the 1980 film that features Robert DeNiro as boxer Jake LaMotta?
A: A bull (*Raging Bull*)

NATURE
Q: Which of these provided painter and naturalist John Audubon's most famous subjects: birds, people, or plants?
A: Birds

FAME
Q: What present-day Hollywood starlet comes from an acting family that includes Lionel, John, and Ethel?
A: Drew Barrymore

BLOCK 36

BLOCK 37

FAME
Q: What name was so popular that the first five Roman emperors used it?
A: Caesar

NATURE
Q: What nocturnal carnivore likes to sneak through the night like a bandit and prefers to wash its food before dining?
A: The raccoon

MEDIA
Q: Who sang the theme song "Nobody Does It Better" from the James Bond movie *The Spy Who Loved Me*: Carly Simon, Sheryl Crow, or Eartha Kitt?
A: Carly Simon

OUR WORLD
Q: Two silly-sounding political groups, the "Know-Nothings" and the "Mugwamps," actually held political sway in what country in the nineteenth century?
A: U.S.

SPORTS
Q: The foil, the epee, and the saber are all used in what Olympic event?
A: Fencing

SCIENCE
Q: Aside from parents and siblings, who are the four closest blood relatives a person can have?
A: Grandparents, uncles, aunts, and children

SCIENCE
Q: Do most submarines use more power to run underwater or on the surface?
A: On the surface

SPORTS
Q: Which kind of board doesn't need wax: skateboard, surfboard, or snowboard?
A: A skateboard

OUR WORLD
Q: Which panhandle state is home to Twin Falls?
A: Idaho

MEDIA
Q: How many minutes are in the title of CBS's top-rated hourly news magazine?
A: 60

NATURE
Q: True or false? Lightning can reach temperatures hotter than the surface of the sun.
A: True

FAME
Q: According to Irish folklore, what treasure can a human obtain if he captures a leprechaun: three wishes, immortality, or a pot of gold?
A: A pot of gold

BLOCK 38

Round 2

FAME
Q: Name the 1920s famous flyer picked by *Time* magazine as its first "Man of the Year."
A: Charles Lindbergh

NATURE
Q: What is the hard-and-fast name of the national park in Arizona that is full of giant fossils?
A: The Petrified Forest

MEDIA
Q: What did the makers of the original Mr. Potato Head® suggest you use for his head?
A: A potato (The original game included just the parts.)

OUR WORLD
Q: In which North American border town can tourists pick up a sombrero before heading back into the U.S. city San Ysidro?
A: Tijuana

SPORTS
Q: Football fans flipped when this team finished with a perfect season in 1972 (17-0). Name the team.
A: Miami Dolphins

SCIENCE
Q: What element of the Periodic Table lends its name to an Age and a Curtain, and is the most common of all metals?
A: Iron

. . . .

SCIENCE
Q: Our Solar System's second largest planet is light enough to float in water. Name the planet.
A: Saturn

SPORTS
Q: The high jumping maneuver invented by Dick Fosbury is called what?
A: The Fosbury Flop

OUR WORLD
Q: What corn-husking state has a capital city named for the sixteenth president of the U.S.?
A: Nebraska (Lincoln)

MEDIA
Q: What letter is adulteress Hester Prynne forced to wear in Nathaniel Hawthorne's novel *The Scarlet Letter*?
A: The letter "A"

NATURE
Q: True or false? Grizzly cubs are usually twins.
A: True

FAME
Q: Name the media mogul whose name shows up everywhere—even in her own production company, Harpo.
A: Oprah Winfrey

BLOCK 3

FAME
Q: What famous Italian lover went by a name that could be translated as "new house"?
A: Casanova

NATURE
Q: What plant is usually depicted rolling through ghost towns, but was often used as a cooked green by Native Americans?
A: The tumbleweed

MEDIA
Q: What is the out-of-this-world first name of *Seinfeld's* Kramer?
A: Cosmo

OUR WORLD
Q: This amazing Roman structure, built in 80 A.D., was the precursor to our modern stadium. What was it called?
A: The Coliseum

SPORTS
Q: What hot-tempered tennis player was ejected from the Australian Open in 1990?
A: John McEnroe

SCIENCE
Q: What big name toothpaste maker revolutionized the industry in 1873 by introducing soap-free dental cream in a jar?
A: Colgate

- -

SCIENCE
Q: Everyone knows that lots and lots of watts are in a gigawatt. But exactly how many?
A: One billion

SPORTS
Q: What is the official "birthday" of all racehorses?
A: January 1

OUR WORLD
Q: What are the four things a bride traditionally wears to her wedding for good luck?
A: Something old, something new, something borrowed, and something blue

MEDIA
Q: In the 1980s flick *Purple Rain*, what was Prince's character's childish name?
A: The Kid

NATURE
Q: What marmot has a U.S. holiday named for it?
A: The groundhog

FAME
Q: What young wanna-be wizard did writer J.K. Rowling create?
A: Harry Potter®

BLOCK 4

BLOCK 5

FAME
Q: Which nineteenth century U.S. president sounds like he could show you around Sesame Street and take you to one of Ohio's biggest cities?
A: Grover Cleveland

NATURE
Q: What is the geographical name of a flat-topped hill for which a city in Montana is named?
A: Butte

MEDIA
Q: What sultry brass instrument does Lisa Simpson play?
A: Saxophone

OUR WORLD
Q: Name the once war-torn country on the South China Sea that has one of the world's largest Buddhist populations.
A: Vietnam

SPORTS
Q: What is the revealing name of the easternmost Major League baseball team in Canada?
A: The Montreal Expos

SCIENCE
Q: Which cannot travel around corners: light waves, heat waves, or sound waves?
A: Light waves

SCIENCE
Q: Who "gave it a shot" and invented the revolver in 1835: Samuel Colt, Richard Gatling, or William Winchester?
A: Samuel Colt

SPORTS
Q: What NASCAR driver "earned" a reputation as one of the greats and died in a tragic 2001 crash?
A: Dale Earnhardt

OUR WORLD
Q: What South American country is named for the imaginary line that passes through it?
A: Ecuador (named for the equator)

MEDIA
Q: What slick song and dance extravaganza starred John Travolta and Olivia Newton-John and was one of the top grossing movies of the 1970s?
A: *Grease*

NATURE
Q: What colorful vegetation is closely associated with the state of Kentucky and a type of music?
A: Bluegrass

FAME
Q: What Dr. Seuss book became a Jim Carrey blockbuster in the 2000 holiday season?
A: *How the Grinch Stole Christmas*

BLOCK 6

BLOCK 7

FAME
Q: What U.S. patriot organized the Boston Tea Party and still helps people party today?
A: Samuel Adams

NATURE
Q: What member of the ox family is found quietly roaming the plateaus of Tibet?
A: The yak

MEDIA
Q: What uplifting phrase does *Star Trek's* Captain Kirk use to return to the Starship Enterprise?
A: Beam me up, Scotty

OUR WORLD
Q: In White House history, what do Fala, Checkers, and Buddy have in common?
A: They were all U.S. presidents' dogs.

SPORTS
Q: True or false? In freestyle swimming events, swimmers may choose any stroke to swim.
A: True (But they almost always chose the crawl because it's the fastest)

SCIENCE
Q: Which of these is the medical name for the funny bone: fibula, humerus, or sternum?
A: Humerus

SCIENCE
Q: Russian space travelers are named from "kosmos" (Greek for universe). What do Russians call their space travelers?
A: Cosmonauts

SPORTS
Q: What baseball team sounds fishy and was the first wild card team to win the World Series?
A: The Florida Marlins

OUR WORLD
Q: What long, skinny South American country sounds cold, but most of it isn't?
A: Chile

MEDIA
Q: According to the title of a popular Elvis Presley song, what color and fabric are his shoes?
A: Blue suede

NATURE
Q: What lush shade plant shares its name with a character from *Charlotte's Web*?
A: Fern

FAME
Q: The "man in black" has a last name that most think of as green. Name this country singer.
A: Johnny Cash

BLOCK 8

BLOCK 9

FAME
Q: What TV captain pals around with Mr. Green Jeans and sounds like a marsupial?
A: Captain Kangaroo

NATURE
Q: True or false? Tigers have striped skin, not just striped fur.
A: True

MEDIA
Q: What film about a lovable creature from space was one of the top grossing movies of the 1980s?
A: *E.T.: The Extra-Terrestrial*

OUR WORLD
Q: Which city in Germany was once divided by a famous wall?
A: Berlin

SPORTS
Q: Which future movie star brought home Olympic gold for Norway in three successive games: 1928, 1932, and 1936?
A: Sonja Henie

SCIENCE
Q: True or false? Flamingos have pink feathers because of their diet.
A: True (They have a diet high in carotenoids, found in algae, shrimp, and insects)

• •

SCIENCE
Q: Humans can't hear sounds at frequencies greater than 20 kHz (kilohertz). Are sounds at 21 kHz called infrasonic or ultrasonic?
A: Ultrasonic

SPORTS
Q: What merry place became the home of the St. Louis Browns when they moved eastward in the 1950s?
A: Baltimore, Maryland

OUR WORLD
Q: In what scenic East African country was the 1985 movie *Out of Africa* filmed?
A: Kenya

MEDIA
Q: Mike Nesmith of the Monkees always sported what trademark accessory?
A: A knit cap

NATURE
Q: Name the bay that is home to Treasure, Yerba Buena, Angel, and Alcatraz islands.
A: The San Francisco Bay

FAME
Q: What centuries-old sucker hates garlic and can often be found "hanging around"?
A: Dracula

BLOCK 10

BLOCK 11

FAME
Q: What actor learned his *Facts of Life* and successfully made the switch from the *ER* to the big screen?
A: George Clooney

NATURE
Q: What South American rodent was never a source of bacon and is now commonly known as a pet and research animal?
A: The guinea pig

MEDIA
Q: Name two of Madonna's first four albums.
A: *Madonna, Like a Virgin, True Blue, You Can Dance*

OUR WORLD
Q: What fierce but graceful animal, one of the largest of the Chinese Zodiac, is near extinction?
A: Tiger

SPORTS
Q: Despite its name, how many teams play in college football's Big 10 Conference?
A: 11

SCIENCE
Q: Human tongues can make out four main tastes. In addition to sweet and sour, name one of the other two.
A: Salt, bitter

• •

SCIENCE
Q: In H_2O, which of these two atoms: hydrogen, oxygen, or helium?
A: Hydrogen

SPORTS
Q: In football, what does hang time measure?
A: The amount of time a punted ball stays in the air

OUR WORLD
Q: What color is caffeine: black, brown, or white?
A: White

MEDIA
Q: Which poet wrote *I Know Why the Caged Bird Sings* and spoke at President Clinton's inauguration?
A: Maya Angelou

NATURE
Q: What luminous phenomenon also goes by the name northern lights?
A: Aurora borealis

FAME
Q: What was the earnest revolutionary Che Guevara's real first name?
A: Ernesto

BLOCK 12

BLOCK 13

FAME
Q: What former U.S. vice president's name sounds like the name for a gamebird?
A: Dan Quayle

NATURE
Q: No ugly duckling, a cygnet is a not-yet-grown-up form of what bird?
A: A swan

MEDIA
Q: Name the sweet-tempered character with a sweet tooth on TV's *Sesame Street*.
A: Cookie Monster

OUR WORLD
Q: Which of these art history luminaries painted first: Picasso, Michelangelo, or Rembrandt?
A: Michelangelo (1475-1564)

SPORTS
Q: Who is the tallest: Michael Jordan, Grant Hill, or Shaquille O'Neal?
A: Shaquille O'Neal

SCIENCE
Q: The sixth planet from the Sun shares the first five letters of its name with a day of the week. Name the planet.
A: Saturn

SCIENCE
Q: Is quantum mechanics (the theory that matter is made up of atoms) part of physics, mechanical engineering, or marine biology?
A: Physics

SPORTS
Q: In world championship play, which team has won more games: the U.S. women's soccer team or the U.S men's soccer team?
A: The U.S women's soccer team

OUR WORLD
Q: Upon your arrest, what are the first four words of the Miranda Rights that you will hear?
A: "You have the right"

MEDIA
Q: What civil war saga made a killing at the box-office in 1939?
A: *Gone With the Wind*

NATURE
Q: Name the treacherous desert that long restricted travel from northern to southern Africa.
A: The Sahara

FAME
Q: Before Ben Stein had a game show on Comedy Central, was he: a ditch digger, a speechwriter for Richard Nixon, or a policeman?
A: A speechwriter for Richard Nixon

BLOCK 14

BLOCK 15

FAME
Q: What famous civil rights leader followed the teachings of Gandhi and was the first president of the Southern Christian Leadership Council?
A: Martin Luther King, Jr.

NATURE
Q: Bred as a beast of burden, the hybrid offspring of a donkey and a horse is called what?
A: A mule

MEDIA
Q: In the lullaby "Hush Little Baby," what is the first thing that momma's gonna buy you?
A: A mockingbird

OUR WORLD
Q: Was Jesus twenty-something or thirty-something when he was crucified by the Romans?
A: Thirty-something (He was 33.)

SPORTS
Q: What Canadian city is home to the Hockey Hall of Fame?
A: Toronto, Ontario

SCIENCE
Q: Does water cover roughly 50, 60, or 70 percent of Earth's surface?
A: 70 percent

SCIENCE
Q: In 1937, 35 people died when the Hindenburg caught fire. Was the Hindenburg a glider, a helicopter or a zeppelin?
A: A zeppelin

SPORTS
Q: The "A.C." in LA Laker A.C. Green's name stands for Arthur Clay Adele Corningsmouth, or nothing?
A: Nothing

OUR WORLD
Q: What ancient Egyptian system of writing used pictures or symbols to stand for words, ideas, or sounds?
A: Hieroglyphics

MEDIA
Q: True or false? Aside from his knowledge of martial arts and weaponry, Batman is a common human, not a superhero.
A: True

NATURE
Q: How many of the seven wonders of the ancient world are man-made?
A: Seven

FAME
Q: Introduced to Americans as Opie Taylor, this successful director helped the Grinch steal Christmas in 2000. Who is he?
A: Ron Howard

BLOCK 16

BLOCK 17

FAME
Q: What famous actor has played roles in Sicily, in Paris, and on the waterfront?
A: Marlon Brando

NATURE
Q: Often cultivated for its beautiful flowers, which tree has a name with a distinctly canine "bark"?
A: Dogwood

MEDIA
Q: What *Animal House* star and first season *Saturday Night Live* alum died of a tragic drug overdose in 1982?
A: John Belushi

OUR WORLD
Q: Which tropical oil has the highest levels of saturated fat of any oil on the market?
A: Coconut oil

SPORTS
Q: True or false? In Olympic volleyball, players are not allowed to serve underhanded.
A: False (Players can serve underhanded, but they almost never do.)

SCIENCE
Q: Who invented the first steel plow: John Deere, Cyrus McCormick, or Avery Plough?
A: John Deere

- -

SCIENCE
Q: During which of these did the first fish appear: Paleozoic, Precambrian, or Cenozoic?
A: Paleozoic

SPORTS
Q: What West Coast team has been victorious every one of the five times it's been to the Super Bowl?
A: The San Francisco 49ers

OUR WORLD
Q: This leader of the Reformation wasn't a king, but he was the first Lutheran. Name him.
A: Martin Luther

MEDIA
Q: What is the zip code for City Hall in Beverly Hills, California?
A: 90210

NATURE
Q: What lethal California gorge holds the record for the most consecutive days with temperatures higher than 120° F?
A: Death Valley

FAME
Q: Which bold Greek goddess was born, without a mother, by springing full-grown from Zeus' head: Aphrodite, Athena, or Artemis?
A: Athena

BLOCK 18

BLOCK 19

FAME
Q: Which artist was labeled "Jack the Dripper" for his revolutionary gestural painting technique and had his life story featured in a 2000 movie?
A: Jackson Pollock

NATURE
Q: Name the four types of winter precipitation.
A: Sleet, snow, hail, and rain

MEDIA
Q: Susan Dey, also known as *The Partridge Family's* Laurie, practiced law on what TV program?
A: *L.A. Law*

OUR WORLD
Q: What geometric lines, or parallels, cover the globe?
A: Lines of latitude

SPORTS
Q: In basketball, what precise penalty allows a player to shoot foul shots with no other players on the same half of the court?
A: A technical foul

SCIENCE
Q: Which of these is not the name of an unmanned U.S. space program: Viking, Victor Victoria, or Voyager?
A: Victor Victoria

• •

SCIENCE
Q: Which of these words refers in an insect to the process of changing from a larva into an adult: egg, pupa, or imago?
A: Pupa

SPORTS
Q: South Africa's first racially-integrated team participated in which Olympics: 1972, 1984, or 1992?
A: 1992

OUR WORLD
Q: What Scandinavian country is home to the Geiranger and Nord Fjords?
A: Norway

MEDIA
Q: What author uses a pseudonym and leads the list of best-selling hardcover children's books of all time?
A: Dr. Seuss (Theodore Geisel)

NATURE
Q: True or false? A dragonfly has an average life span of 24 hours.
A: True

FAME
Q: What band had a number one album on the Billboard Charts in 2001, but has been broken up since 1970?
A: The Beatles

BLOCK 20

BLOCK 21

FAME
Q: What U.S. president unwittingly started a stuffed toy animal craze after refusing to shoot a captive bear cub during a 1902 hunting trip?
A: Teddy Roosevelt

NATURE
Q: Which of these factors does not contribute to the greenhouse effect: trapped gases, acid rain, or burning fossil fuel?
A: Acid rain

MEDIA
Q: What major religion sponsors the Tabernacle Choir?
A: The Mormon Church

OUR WORLD
Q: What is the name of the national lawmaking body of Great Britain: Congress, Buckingham Palace, or Parliament?
A: Parliament

SPORTS
Q: Who is the much-quoted sage who has been called the best "bad ball" hitter in baseball and has something in common with a famous bear?
A: Yogi Berra

SCIENCE
Q: True or false? Henry Ford invented and sold the first gas-powered automobile in 1885.
A: False (It was Karl Benz.)

• •

SCIENCE
Q: Name the five basic human sensory organs.
A: Eyes, ears, nose, tongue, skin

SPORTS
Q: Who won five consecutive Wimbledon championships in 1976–1980 and shares his last name with a Star Trek villain?
A: Björn Borg

OUR WORLD
Q: This historical figure ruled Rome before the birth of Christ and shares his name with a hip haircut.
A: Julius Caesar

MEDIA
Q: What is the name of the Holy Book of Islam: the Ahmad, the Koran, or the Torah?
A: The Koran (or Qur'an)

NATURE
Q: What is the name of the sea that lies between Great Britain and Ireland?
A: The Irish Sea

FAME
Q: Under what name did rapper Robert VanWinkle rocket to fame—and notoriety—in the early 1990s?
A: Vanilla Ice

BLOCK 22

FAME
Q: According to Paul Simon's hit song, how many ways are there to leave your lover?
A: 50

NATURE
Q: Of the world's 50 highest mountains, how many are not in Asia?
A: None

MEDIA
Q: Who are the two sassy girl characters in the comic strip *Archie*?
A: Veronica and Betty

OUR WORLD
Q: What nineteenth century land purchase was referred to as both Seward's Icebox and Seward's Folly?
A: Alaska

SPORTS
Q: In a 12-month period, do more people attend professional football, NASCAR racing, or professional golf tournaments?
A: NASCAR racing

SCIENCE
Q: Archaeopteryx fossils provide a link between birds and which of these animals: dinosaurs, bats, or giraffes?
A: Dinosaurs

SCIENCE
Q: Which of these products causes sugar to ferment: yeast, salt, or baking soda?
A: Yeast

SPORTS
Q: The USTTA, founded in 1933, governs tournament competition in the U.S. for what sport?
A: Table tennis

OUR WORLD
Q: Which two mid-Atlantic states gave up land to create our nation's capital, Washington, D.C.?
A: Maryland and Virginia

MEDIA
Q: What cunning forest animal has the same name as Mulder on *The X-Files*?
A: The Fox

NATURE
Q: What breed of small dog is named for the Mexican state where it originated?
A: The Chihuahua

FAME
Q: What musician spent a week in bed protesting for peace and played with Paul McCartney in the Quarrymen?
A: John Lennon

BLOCK 25

FAME
Q: Actress Grace Kelly became princess of what principality when she married Prince Rainier?
A: Monaco

NATURE
Q: True or false? You can only see a rainbow if you are not facing the sun.
A: True

MEDIA
Q: What 1992 vampire spoof movie launched a successful TV series starring Sarah Michelle Gellar?
A: *Buffy the Vampire Slayer*

OUR WORLD
Q: World War I began soon after a Serbian patriot shot an Austrian prince in Sarajevo. Is Sarajevo in the Baltics, the Balkans, or the Hebrides?
A: The Balkans

SPORTS
Q: Which famous skater is not from the U.S.: Peggy Fleming, Eric Heiden, Kristi Yamaguchi, or Wayne Gretsky?
A: Wayne Gretsky (He hails from Canada.)

SCIENCE
Q: Which type of electrical current does not alternate, moving in only one direction: AC or DC?
A: DC (direct current)

• •

SCIENCE
Q: What must happen to the water in an ice cube before it can evaporate?
A: It must melt and turn to liquid.

SPORTS
Q: What is the colorful punishment for extreme fouls in soccer?
A: A yellow card

OUR WORLD
Q: What decorative yet functional device is among the most common things hung on the walls in people's homes?
A: A clock

MEDIA
Q: What unlikely love story, animated by Disney, was one of the top grossing movies in the 1950s?
A: *Lady and the Tramp*

NATURE
Q: What gas in the atmosphere protects life from the sun's harmful rays?
A: Ozone

FAME
Q: How many kids did Elvis "the Pelvis" have?
A: One, Lisa Marie Presley

BLOCK 26

BLOCK 27

FAME
Q: Name the classic wooden toy set that bears a president's name.
A: Lincoln Logs®

NATURE
Q. What pungent Australian gum tree is actually a member of the myrtle family?
A. Eucalyptus

MEDIA
Q: In what rocking hit from the 1980s does David Bowie suggest we "put on our red shoes and dance the blues"?
A: "Let's Dance"

OUR WORLD
Q: Which religion is practiced by more people than any other?
A: Christianity

SPORTS
Q: What is the top number of points possible on a single shot in darts?
A: 60 (for a triple in darts)

SCIENCE
Q: Which of these devices was not invented by Thomas Alva Edison: the light bulb, the motion picture projector, or the X-ray machine?
A: The X-ray machine (invented by Wilhelm Conrad Roentgen)

• •

SCIENCE
Q: Is the shape of a DNA molecule a helix, a double helix, or an ellipse?
A: A double helix

SPORTS
Q: The U.S. first hosted the Olympic Games in what city: Los Angeles, Lake Placid, or Saint Louis?
A: Saint Louis, Missouri in 1904

OUR WORLD
Q: Which gentlemanly state was the birthplace of four of the first five U.S. presidents?
A: Virginia

MEDIA
Q: According to the song, what does "This Old Man" play knick-knack on?
A: My thumb, my shoe, my knee, or my door

NATURE
Q: Are polar bears faster swimmers or runners?
A: Runners (up to 35 mph)

FAME
Q: Lucy Lawless plays what royal warrior on TV?
A: Xena Warrior Princess

BLOCK 28

BLOCK 29

FAME
Q: What well-known reggae rocker wrote Eric Clapton's number-one hit, "I Shot the Sheriff"?
A: Bob Marley

NATURE
Q: Which country experiences the most tornadoes each year?
A: The United States

MEDIA
Q: What good guy played husband to TV's *Roseanne*?
A: John Goodman

OUR WORLD
Q: Which Italian city is known for a famous tilting tower?
A: Pisa

SPORTS
Q: The NFL and the AFL merged in what year: 1960, 1970, or 1980?
A: 1970

SCIENCE
Q: Not including the thumb, what are the common names of the four fingers on a human hand?
A: Index finger (or pointer), middle finger, ring finger, and pinkie

• •

SCIENCE
Q: What keeps earthlings grounded?
A: Gravity!

SPORTS
Q: How many seconds are allowed on the NBA shot clock: 18, 22, or 24?
A: 24

OUR WORLD
Q: What top-selling medicinal herb is said to ward off depression naturally?
A: St. John's Wort

MEDIA
Q: What "wild" Hollywood moviemaker directed *The Apartment* and *Some Like It Hot*?
A: Billy Wilder

NATURE
Q: Is a group of lions called a bevy, a pride, or a pack?
A: A pride

FAME
Q: What family singing group sold 10 million records in nine months in 1970?
A: The Jackson 5

BLOCK 30

BLOCK 31

FAME	Q: What gift did sweet-natured Little Red Riding Hood bring "over the river and through the woods" for her grandmother? A: Cakes
NATURE	Q: What seed coat is the main ingredient of a popular kind of muffin? A: Bran
MEDIA	Q: Which galaxy shares its name with a strain in a science fiction thriller by Michael Crichton? A: Andromeda (*The Andromeda Strain*)
OUR WORLD	Q: What fifth century leader was "X-ed" out in his attempt to conquer Greece? A: Xerxes
SPORTS	Q: In 1992, what female player became the youngest ever inducted into the Tennis Hall of Fame? A: Tracy Austin
SCIENCE	Q: Which of these gases makes up 78% of the air in Earth's lower atmosphere: helium, nitrogen, or petroleum? A: Nitrogen

• •

SCIENCE	Q: For what x-traordinary discovery did Wilhelm Roentgen win a Nobel Prize in 1901? A: The X-ray
SPORTS	Q: In horse racing, if a horse "shows," in what place did it finish? A: Third place
OUR WORLD	Q: On the good ol' Stars and Stripes, are there more red stripes or white stripes? A: Red stripes
MEDIA	Q: What *Cheers* spin-off features a neurotic psychiatrist living in Seattle? A: *Frasier*
NATURE	Q: As a percentage of its total body length, roughly how long does an alligator's tail grow to be: 20%, 50%, or 80%? A: 50%
FAME	Q: What Civil War general and American president shares his name with a Greek war hero? A: Ulysses Simpson Grant

BLOCK 32

BLOCK 33

FAME
Q: Who was the sidekick of the clay-mation character Gumby?
A: Pokey

NATURE
Q: What is the most common cause of a tidal wave: atmospheric pressure colliding with a jet stream, earthquake, or extremely intense winds?
A: Earthquake

MEDIA
Q: 1980s hitmakers Duran Duran sang the theme song to which killer James Bond movie?
A: *View To a Kill*

OUR WORLD
Q: Name the Canadian capital city that starts with O.
A: Ottawa

SPORTS
Q: In what sport do contestants battle to win the Ryder Cup: golf, tennis, or tractor pulls?
A: Golf

SCIENCE
Q: When the moon blocks Earth's view of the sun, does it cause a lunar eclipse or a solar eclipse?
A: A solar eclipse

· ·

SCIENCE
Q: By what process do green plants use the energy of light to make food from carbon dioxide and water?
A: Photosynthesis

SPORTS
Q: Name the player who, before he was banned from baseball, nicknamed one of his bats Black Betsey.
A: "Shoeless" Joe Jackson

OUR WORLD
Q: What desert city boasts the most hotel rooms of any U.S. city?
A: Las Vegas, NV

MEDIA
Q: Which magazine sells the most copies (newsstand plus subscription): *National Geographic*, *TV Guide*, or *Readers Digest*?
A: *Readers Digest*

NATURE
Q: India and China are separated by what mountain range?
A: The Himalayas

FAME
Q: Name two of the many actors in *Fast Times at Ridgemont High* that went on to become well-known celebrities.
A: Sean Penn, Jennifer Jason Leigh, Judge Reinhold, Eric Stoltz, Anthony Edwards, Phoebe Cates, Forest Whitaker or Nicholas Cage

BLOCK 34

BLOCK 35

FAME
Q: What diva sang the song "People" in the movie *Funny Girl*?
A: Barbra Streisand

NATURE
Q: What common farm animal feed is typically composed of dried clover, alfalfa, or timothy?
A: Hay

MEDIA
Q: What was the spacey name of the Jetson family dog: Meteor, Astro, or Moon?
A: Astro

OUR WORLD
Q: Which tiny European country starts with the letter "L" and has a name that sounds like a cartoon-obsessed American Pop artist?
A: Liechtenstein

SPORTS
Q: At 19, George Foreman won an Olympic gold metal in boxing. Was he 40, 45, or 50 when he won his second heavyweight boxing title?
A: 45 years old

SCIENCE
Q: In humans, which teeth are the best suited to chewing food: incisors, canines, or molars?
A: Molars

• •

SCIENCE
Q: True or false? Catalysts speed up or slow down chemical reactions and are not changed in the process.
A: True

SPORTS
Q: In which of these sports do athletes explore caves: orienteering, takraw, or spelunking?
A: Spelunking

OUR WORLD
Q: When Charles Martel defeated the Moors at the Battle of Tours in 732 A.D., what mountain range did the Moors have to cross to get from France to Spain?
A: The Pyrenees

MEDIA
Q: In E. B. White's classic children's book about a spider, what is the name of the pig character?
A: Wilbur the Pig (From *Charlotte's Web*)

NATURE
Q: On average, which ocean is the deepest: the Atlantic or the Pacific?
A: The Pacific Ocean

FAME
Q: What does it mean when the Queen of England issues a "Royal Warrant:" legal trouble, a mark of recognition, or a request to visit Buckingham Palace?
A: A mark of recognition

BLOCK 36

FAME
Q: This six-time Wimbledon champion has a name that suggests royalty. Who is she?
A: Billie Jean King

NATURE
Q: True or false? A tarantula bite is poisonous, even deadly.
A: False (Tarantulas are not dangerous to humans.)

MEDIA
Q: What cartoon character uses snacks to motivate his canine cohort and has a disheveled appearance that hints at his name?
A: Shaggy

OUR WORLD
Q: Which U.S. state capital has a name that means "small boulder"?
A: Little Rock, Arkansas

SPORTS
Q: What baseball superstar hitter holds the record for strikeouts with 2,957: Babe Ruth, Mark McGwire, or Reggie Jackson?
A: Reggie Jackson

SCIENCE
Q: In 1924, who devised a process for freezing food to preserve it: Clarence Birdseye, Sarah Lee, or Lewis Waterman?
A: Clarence Birdseye

SCIENCE
Q: Ultraviolet rays are beyond what color in the visible spectrum?
A: Violet

SPORTS
Q: What year was basketball believed to be invented: 1891, 1911, or 1931?
A: 1891

OUR WORLD
Q: Which ocean lends a letter to the acronym NATO?
A: Atlantic Ocean

MEDIA
Q: Who was the keyboard player for The Doors: Ray Manzarek, Robby Krieger, or John Densmore?
A: Ray Manzarek

NATURE
Q: What do scientists call the leader of a wolf pack: the alpha, the beta, or the dancer?
A: The alpha

FAME
Q: Who was Argentina's famous first lady, portrayed by Madonna on the big screen?
A: Evita

Round 3

BLOCK 1

FAME
Q: Which former Israeli Prime Minister was a decorated soldier and shares his first name with a famous Franklin?
A: Benjamin Netanyahu

NATURE
Q: What animal's name, Afrikaans for "earth pig," ensures it is always first alphabetically?
A: The aardvark

MEDIA
Q: What superhero did Peter Parker become after he was bitten by a radioactive spider?
A: Spider-Man

OUR WORLD
Q: Which country boasts the world's northernmost capital city, Reykjavik, and is home to pop sensation Bjork?
A: Iceland

SPORTS
Q: In what sport might a successful turn not count if you don't call the bank first?
A: Billiards

SCIENCE
Q: Which sleep disorder is known as somnambulism: snoring, bedwetting, or sleepwalking?
A: Sleepwalking

SCIENCE
Q: The coccyx, attached to the base of the human spine, is the evolutionary remainder of what body part?
A: A tail

SPORTS
Q: Hockey player Dale Hunter holds the dubious distinction of most times spent where during the NHL playoffs?
A: In the penalty box (691 minutes!)

OUR WORLD
Q: What word not found in this sentence is used most often in American English?
A: The

MEDIA
Q: What regal color is Harold's crayon in Crockett Johnson's book series?
A: Purple

NATURE
Q: What purple-blossomed plant was long the favorite traditional scent of men's grooming products?
A: Lavender

FAME
Q: What daytime talk show host got a new gig and took his ABC show to number one in 2000?
A: Regis Philbin

BLOCK 2

47

BLOCK 3

FAME
Q: According to American folklore, this legendary hero of the lumber camps cut the Grand Canyon by dragging his pick behind him.
A: Paul Bunyan

NATURE
Q: Polar bears cover a part of their body with a paw so that they can't be seen as easily while hunting. Name the part.
A: The nose

MEDIA
Q: What 1999 low-budget hit was filmed with a hand-held camera and had a bewitching effect on audiences around the globe?
A: *The Blair Witch Project*

OUR WORLD
Q: Alexander Hamilton is the only non-president who appears on U.S. paper money worth less than $50. How much is his bill worth?
A: $10

SPORTS
Q: In 1947, which boundary-breaking player won the first National League Rookie of the Year Award?
A: Jackie Robinson

SCIENCE
Q: The symbol for the first element of the Periodic Table is "H." Does it stand for hydrogen, helium, or haluminum?
A: Hydrogen

• •

SCIENCE
Q: What code did Francis Crick help crack in the early 1950s?
A: The genetic code

SPORTS
Q: In football, what is the lowly name for an offensive attempt to advance 10 yards on the field?
A: A down

OUR WORLD
Q: What three midwestern states, all starting with the letter "I," could you drive through in succession?
A: Iowa, Illinois, and Indiana

MEDIA
Q: What sit-com "improved" the career of teen heartthrob Jonathan Taylor Thomas?
A: *Home Improvement*

NATURE
Q: What triangular deposit of sediment forms when a river flows into the sea, and shares its name with a triangular Greek letter?
A: A delta

FAME
Q: Name the president whose last name makes him sound like an honest guy.
A: Harry S. Truman

BLOCK 4

BLOCK 5

FAME
Q: Name the famous Disney parrot that shares his name with the villain from Shakespeare's *Othello*.
A: Iago (Disney's *Aladdin*)

NATURE
Q: Name the yellow or green fruit that is likely to split for dessert.
A: Banana

MEDIA
Q: What money-minded New York street provides the title of the 1987 movie in which Michael Douglas plays financier Gordon Gekko?
A: *Wall Street*

OUR WORLD
Q: What top-selling medicinal herb is said to fight off colds and flu?
A: Echinacea

SPORTS
Q: In cycling, what's the name for a race in which cyclists start at opposite sides of an oval track and try to pass: a pursuit, a chase, or a sprint?
A: A pursuit

SCIENCE
Q: What element of the periodic table shares its name with a unit of U.S. currency?
A: Nickel

· ·

SCIENCE
Q: Which planet in our solar system is usually the hottest?
A: Venus

SPORTS
Q: What are the "cute" depressions in a golf ball called?
A: Dimples

OUR WORLD
Q: In what U.S. state are you likely to get lei'd?
A: Hawaii

MEDIA
Q: What is the quiet-sounding title of Simon & Garfunkel's first number one hit?
A: "The Sound of Silence"

NATURE
Q: What baby mammal grows for almost two years in its mother's womb before it is born: an elephant, a dog, or a kangaroo?
A: Elephant

FAME
Q: In what John Hughes movie did Molly Ringwald have a birthday?
A: *Sixteen Candles*

BLOCK 6

BLOCK 7

FAME
Q: To this scantily clad "swinger," it's a jungle out there. Who is he?
A: Tarzan

NATURE
Q: What 217 mile-long gorge was formed by erosion from the Colorado River?
A: The Grand Canyon

MEDIA
Q: What *Addams Family* character shares her name with a day of the week?
A: Wednesday

OUR WORLD
Q: Name three of the five fruity colors of 1999's Apple iMacs.
A: Blueberry, grape, tangerine, strawberry, and lime

SPORTS
Q: Sandy Koufax pitched for the same team in two different hometowns. What was the team?
A: The Dodgers (Brooklyn and Los Angeles)

SCIENCE
Q: Who mixed things up and perfected a process that kills bacteria in milk: John Carnation, Pierre Curie, or Louis Pasteur?
A: Louis Pasteur

• •

SCIENCE
Q: When a light beam passes through glass, will it bend or continue in a straight line?
A: Bend or refract

SPORTS
Q: Name the basketball player, notorious for his off-court exploits, who scored the most points in a season with 4,029 in 1961–62.
A: Wilt Chamberlain

OUR WORLD
Q: What wondrous man-made barrier in China is visible, without a telescope, from the moon?
A: The Great Wall of China

MEDIA
Q: In what language was Leo Tolstoy's epic *War and Peace* first published?
A: Russian

NATURE
Q: Name the member of the viper family that tries to let you know it's coming.
A: The rattlesnake

FAME
Q: What kind of night does Vincent Van Gogh's famous painting feature?
A: A "Starry Night"

BLOCK 8

BLOCK 9

FAME
Q: Which U.S. president coined the phrase, "Read my lips. No new taxes" in his campaign speech?
A: George Bush

NATURE
Q: Which of the world's oceans is the largest, covering one third of the earth's surface?
A: The Pacific

MEDIA
Q: Which *South Park* character is seriously injured in every episode: Cartman, Chef, or Kenny?
A: Kenny

OUR WORLD
Q: Henry VIII had a bad habit of beheading his wives. How many survived him at his death in 1547?
A: Two (Anne of Cleves, Catherine Parr)

SPORTS
Q: In what year did mouthpieces become mandatory equipment in the NFL: 1961, 1971, or 1981?
A: 1971

SCIENCE
Q: Is a turkey's second stomach called a giblet, a wattle, or a gizzard?
A: A gizzard

SCIENCE
Q: What type of fuel is used to power a Bunsen burner?
A: Gas

SPORTS
Q: True or false? The first "baskets" in basketball were actually milk pails.
A: False (They were close-bottomed peach baskets)

OUR WORLD
Q: What state capital shares its name with a bird that rises from the ashes?
A: Phoenix, AZ

MEDIA
Q: Which actress is the only woman to ever win four Academy Awards® for Best Actress and often starred opposite Spencer Tracy?
A: Katharine Hepburn

NATURE
Q: What do you call a fertile tract of land supported by an underground spring and surrounded by desert?
A: An oasis

FAME
Q: What TV funnyman captivated the imagination of millions with a show about nothing in the 1990s?
A: Jerry Seinfeld

BLOCK 10

BLOCK 11

FAME
Q: Name the prophet who survived three days and three nights in the belly of a whale.
A: Jonah

NATURE
Q: What animal has been a companion to mankind for more than 12,000 years and boasts over 400 breeds?
A: The dog

MEDIA
Q: What city did Godzilla destroy?
A: Tokyo

OUR WORLD
Q: Name the majestic white church high on a Paris hill whose name means "sacred heart."
A: Sacre Coeur

SPORTS
Q: What game are you playing when you "run the table"?
A: Pool

SCIENCE
Q: True or false? Propulsion causes an object thrown in the air to return to the ground.
A: False (Gravity causes objects to return.)

• •

SCIENCE
Q: When Whitcomb L. Judson developed the zipper in 1893, what prior clothing system did he intend to replace?
A: Buttons

SPORTS
Q: The NFL record-holder for receiving touchdowns also shares his name with the world's most popular food staple. Who is he?
A: Jerry Rice

OUR WORLD
Q: If you are lactose intolerant, what types of food do you have trouble digesting?
A: Dairy products

MEDIA
Q: What are the times of year named in Vivaldi's *Four Seasons?*
A: Spring, summer, fall, winter

NATURE
Q: El Azizia recorded the world's highest temperature (136° F.). Which continent contains El Azizia?
A: Africa

FAME
Q: Queen Noor of Jordan, born Lisa Najeeb Halaby, was born and educated in what English-speaking country?
A: The United States

BLOCK 12

BLOCK 13

FAME
Q: What British character wears a cloak and works closely with Watson?
A: Sherlock Holmes

NATURE
Q: Which type of cloud is typically large, fluffy, and white: stratus, cirrus, or cumulus?
A: Cumulus

MEDIA
Q: Who was Speed Racer's girlfriend: Pixie, Trixie, or Dixie?
A: Trixie

OUR WORLD
Q: In 1950, the U.S. sent soldiers to fight in the Korean War. Were they fighting for North, South, East, or West Korea?
A: South Korea

SPORTS
Q: Association Football is another name for what sport?
A: Soccer

SCIENCE
Q: Did the compact disc first hit store shelves in 1970, 1980, or 1990?
A: 1980

• •

SCIENCE
Q: How many bones are in a normal human skeleton: 206, 510, or 1,299?
A: 206

SPORTS
Q: What Olympic sport does an athlete called a bobber compete in?
A: Bobsledding

OUR WORLD
Q: What is the name of the highland in North America that separates the waters flowing into the Atlantic Ocean from those flowing in to the Pacific Ocean?
A: The Continental Divide

MEDIA
Q: Name the British TV show that stars the large, lovable characters Po, Dipsy, Tinky Winky and Laa-Laa?
A: *Teletubbies*

NATURE
Q: Which of the following treats is made from a tree: Jell-O, ice cream, or chewing gum?
A: Chewing gum

FAME
Q: What celebrated Irish-American icon was the first Catholic president of the U.S.?
A: John F. Kennedy

BLOCK 14

BLOCK 15

FAME
Q: Janet Jackson has lots of talented brothers besides Michael. Which of these people is *not* one of her brothers: Jackie, Jemaine, or Jamal?
A: Jamal

NATURE
Q: At up to 10 feet long and 300 pounds, the Komodo Dragon is the worlds largest animal of what species?
A: Lizard

MEDIA
Q: What is the newfangled name of the lead character in the movie *The Matrix*?
A: Neo

OUR WORLD
Q: What 1964 Republican presidential candidate issued bumper stickers reading AuH_2O?
A: Barry Goldwater

SPORTS
Q: The 1916, 1940, and 1944 Olympic games were all canceled for the same reason. What was it?
A: War (World War I and World War II)

SCIENCE
Q: True or false? Petroleum forms naturally from dead plants and animals.
A: True

- -

SCIENCE
Q: Besides solid and liquid, what is the third physical state of matter?
A: Gas

SPORTS
Q: What little gymnast with a big smile was the first American woman to win an Olympic gold medal in individual gymnastics competition?
A: Mary Lou Retton

OUR WORLD
Q: Benazir Bhutto is the first woman to rule a predominantly Muslim country. Name this country, a neighbor of India.
A: Pakistan

MEDIA
Q: In what 1977 movie does Richard Dreyfuss get very close to alien beings?
A: *Close Encounters of the Third Kind*

NATURE
Q: True or false? The last known explosion of Vesuvius, the Italian volcano that destroyed Pompeii, occurred when it buried the ancient city.
A: False (Vesuvius is still active today)

FAME
Q: Name the nineteenth century author whose last name sounds like Texas' capital city.
A: Jane Austen

BLOCK 16

BLOCK 17

FAME
Q: Which U.S. president can take credit for the creation of the blueberry-flavored Jelly Belly® jellybean?
Q: Ronald Reagan

NATURE
Q: Which of these atmospheric zones is farthest from Earth: exosphere, ionosphere, mesosphere, stratosphere, or troposphere?
A: Exosphere

MEDIA
Q: What national newspaper sells more copies each day than any other daily newspaper in the U.S.A.?
A: *USA Today* (more than 1.5 million)

OUR WORLD
Q: What is the common coffee drink that combines espresso and milk foam, and is often served in a bowl-like mug?
A: Cappuccino

SPORTS
Q: The NBA's Bucks play for what city renowned for its brew?
A: Milwaukee

SCIENCE
Q: Which of Earth's neighbors has potato-shaped moons named Deimos and Phobos?
A: Mars

• •

SCIENCE
Q: In what season is the sun closest to the U.S. and Canada?
A: Winter

SPORTS
Q: Which young woman won the U.S. Open, the Australian Open and Wimbledon titles in 1997—and shares her first name with another tennis great?
A: Martina Hingis

OUR WORLD
Q: In 1066, William the Conqueror led the battle of the Saxons versus the Normans in England. Was William a Norman or a Saxon?
A: A Norman

MEDIA
Q: During what decade did Robert Moog invent the electric synthesizer?
A: The 1960s

NATURE
Q: Popular in home aquariums, what heavenly sea creature features a sharp spine on each cheek?
A: The angelfish

FAME
Q: Drummer Richard Starkey dropped the "key" from his last name. By what name does the world know him?
A: Ringo Starr

BLOCK 18

FAME
Q: Name the political leader whose 1948 assassination was seen as an international catastrophe.
A: Mahatma Gandhi

NATURE
Q: What colorful succulent shares its name with a precious stone?
A: The jade plant

MEDIA
Q: Beatrix Potter wrote about four rabbits. Three of them were named Flopsy, Mopsy, and Cotton-tail. What was the fourth named?
A: Peter

OUR WORLD
Q: What majestic month, known for its dog days, has no major religious or national holidays in the U.S.?
A: August

SPORTS
Q: How many times do cars go around the track in the Indianapolis 500: 200, 250, or 500?
A: 200 (The track is 2.5 miles around.)

SCIENCE
Q: What did the 1996 Telecommunications Act require TV manufacturers to install in new sets so owners could filter out violent programming?
A: A computer chip, popularly known as the v-chip.

SCIENCE
Q: Which of these medical terms describes the study of old age and its diseases: ageology, geriatrics, or pediatrics?
A: Geriatrics

SPORTS
Q: Winning the championship of which professional sport earns an athlete the most money: heavyweight boxing, football, or baseball?
A: Boxing

OUR WORLD
Q: Is the sixteenth century rebirth of ideas, culture and political thought called The Reformation or The Renaissance?
A: The Renaissance

MEDIA
Q: According to the title of Cole Porter's 1948 musical, what should Kate do?
A: Kiss me

NATURE
Q: What do Louisville Sluggers, a tree, and a religious Wednesday have in common?
A: Ash

FAME
Q: The Queen's short-legged companions of Welsh origin, Phoenix, Kelpie, and Swift, are what breed of dog?
A: Corgi!

BLOCK 21

FAME
Q: Which of these women founded the American Red Cross in 1882: Emily Cross, Florence Nightingale, or Clara Barton?
A: Clara Barton

NATURE
Q: What European country, often victimized by avalanches, is home to the Snow and Avalanche Research Institute?
A: Switzerland

MEDIA
Q: On what Fox hit does Peter MacNicol play an attorney known as "The Biscuit" who who idolizes Barry White?
A: *Ally McBeal*

OUR WORLD
Q: Name three of the four countries in which the Alps are found.
A: France, Switzerland, Italy, and Austria

SPORTS
Q: How long is an Olympiad?
A: Four years

SCIENCE
Q: True or false? The triceratops' tail was longer than its body.
A: False

SCIENCE
Q: True or false? On a clear night, you can see about three billion stars with the naked eye.
A: False (You can only(!) see about 30,000 stars)

SPORTS
Q: What nation is credited with inventing soccer?
A: England

OUR WORLD
Q: This "towering" office building is the tallest in the world and shares its name with a department store.
A: Sears Tower

MEDIA
Q: In what movie does Al Pacino play drug lord Tony Montana?
A: *Scarface*

NATURE
Q: True or false? Some frogs eat so many fireflies that they themselves start to glow.
A: True

FAME
Q: What rootin'-tootin' Looney Tunes© character shares his first name with a national park?
A: Yosemite Sam

BLOCK 22

BLOCK 23

FAME
Q: Marion Morrison showed true grit when he changed his name for films. What was his stage name?
A: John Wayne

NATURE
Q: What nautical green plant can be found in most Japanese restaurants?
A: Seaweed

MEDIA
Q: What is the most frequently sung song in the English language, and is heard at joyous celebrations?
A: "Happy Birthday to You"

OUR WORLD
Q: What diminutive French ruler was defeated at the Battle of Waterloo and now has a complex named after him?
A: Napoleon Bonaparte

SPORTS
Q: In baseball, what does the hitter call the spot six to eight inches down from the wide end of the bat?
A: The sweet spot

SCIENCE
Q: What is the name of the layer of the earth that lies between the crust and the core—and sounds like it belongs above a fireplace?
A: The mantle

• •

SCIENCE
Q: What is the highest Celsius temperature at which water freezes?
A: Zero degrees

SPORTS
Q: Name the prestigious west coast university that was the NCAA Champion of Champions from 1994–1999.
A: Stanford University

OUR WORLD
Q: Pilsner Urquell brand beer is made in what European republic?
A: Czech Republic

MEDIA
Q: What wacky poem by Lewis Carroll begins, "Twas brillig and the slithy toves…"?
A: Jabberwocky

NATURE
Q: What is the name of the world's largest gulf?
A: The Gulf of Mexico

FAME
Q: The first president to appear on television did so in 1939 at the New York World's Fair. Who was it?
A: Franklin D. Roosevelt

BLOCK 24

BLOCK 25

FAME
Q: What is the Jewish Festival of Lights also known as?
A: Hanukkah or Chanukah

NATURE
Q: What is the common name for a pyrite, a mineral which many miners mistakenly thought would make them rich?
A: Fool's gold

MEDIA
Q: Did child star Todd Bridges play Willis or Arnold in the 1970s sit-com *Different Strokes*?
A: Willis

OUR WORLD
Q: How many people usually sit on a "jury of your peers" in a U.S. courtroom?
A: 12

SPORTS
Q: In 1924, what Boston team became the first U.S. member of the NHL?
A: The Bruins

SCIENCE
Q: The same side of the moon always faces the earth—true or false?
A: True

• •

SCIENCE
Q: Does the human body have more bones or more muscles?
A: More muscles (roughly 600 total)

SPORTS
Q: What tennis player has something in common with a famous intern and was stabbed by a Steffi Graf fan in 1993?
A: Monica Seles has the same first name as Monica Lewinsky, White House intern.

OUR WORLD
Q: India declared independence from Britain in 1947. Name one of the two neighboring countries that declared independence from India in 1947.
A: West Pakistan, East Pakistan (Bangladesh)

MEDIA
Q: What is the last phrase of the "Star Spangled Banner"?
A: "And the home of the brave"

NATURE
Q: True or false? One glacier covers roughly 90% of Antarctica.
A: True

FAME
Q: What city contains the famous Abbey Road?
A: London

BLOCK 26

GAME OF KNOWLEDGE

BLOCK 27

FAME
Q: Name three of the four famous rock stars who burned out instead of fading away and died at the age of 27.
A: Janis Joplin, Jimi Hendrix, Jim Morrison, and Kurt Cobain

NATURE
Q: What is the most popular type of pet in the United States?
A: The cat

MEDIA
Q: What type of music features "headbanging"?
A: Heavy metal

OUR WORLD
Q: What two continents are located completely in the Southern Hemisphere?
A: Australia, Antarctica

SPORTS
Q: Imposing Hakeem Olajuwan has done what more than 3,400 times in his NBA career?
A: Blocked a shot

SCIENCE
Q: What do you call a dark area in space that has a gravitational field so intense that even light can't escape?
A: A black hole

- -

SCIENCE
Q: Does the burning of coal, oil, and gas increase or decrease the amount of carbon dioxide in the atmosphere?
A: Increase

SPORTS
Q: How long is a regulation football game?
A: 60 minutes (four 15-minute quarters)

OUR WORLD
Q: Which oil company owned the tanker that ran aground in Alaska's Prince William Sound in 1989, causing one of the worst oil spills in history?
A: Exxon

MEDIA
Q: Charles Foster Kane utters what flowery name just before his death in *Citizen Kane*?
A: Rosebud

NATURE
Q: What is the only metal that is a liquid at room temperature?
A: Mercury

FAME
Q: Name the Trojan warrior from *The Iliad* who shares his name with the "City of Lights."
A: Paris

BLOCK 28

BLOCK 29

FAME
Q: What speedy hedgehog stars in many of Sega's© games?
A: Sonic

NATURE
Q: True or false? An electrical storm features the same scientific principles as the static electricity you can create when you rub your feet on a carpet and shock the next thing you touch.
A: True

MEDIA
Q: Which Beatles song claims that money can't purchase romance, and was one of their biggest hits?
A: "Can't Buy Me Love"

OUR WORLD
Q: Which two continents, named after explorer Amerigo Vespucci, make up the Western Hemisphere?
A: North America, South America

SPORTS
Q: Some bowlers do not use bowling alleys. On what surface do they bowl?
A: Grass (Lawn bowling)

SCIENCE
Q: Who invented the bicycle tire in 1888: John Dunlop, Charles Goodyear, or Daisy Tandem?
A: John Dunlop

- -

SCIENCE
Q: Piltdown Man was a hoax using a human skull with an ape's jaw attached. What did it "prove" a link between?
A: Humans and apes (the "missing" link)

SPORTS
Q: Which of these racetracks hosts the Kentucky Derby: Belmont Park, Churchill Downs, or Pimlico?
A: Churchill Downs

OUR WORLD
Q: Name the Delaware city that shares its name with white cliffs in England.
A: Dover

MEDIA
Q: What American showman started "The Greatest Show on Earth" and said, "There's a sucker born every minute."?
A: P. T. Barnum

NATURE
Q: Roughly half of the world's population depends on which grain as a dietary staple?
A: Rice

FAME
Q: What upstart movie director takes it on the chin for refusing to join the Director's Guild of America?
A: Quentin Tarantino

BLOCK 30

FAME
Q: Who parted the Red Sea—Paul, Jesus, or Moses?
A: Moses

NATURE
Q: Does the Equator divide Earth into east and west, or north and south?
A: North and South

MEDIA
Q: What *Star Wars* "pre-quel" was released in 1999?
A: *Episode 1, The Phantom Menace*

OUR WORLD
Q: In what sunny states are Disney's American theme parks located?
A: California and Florida

SPORTS
Q: What is the "legal" number of points needed to win a game of ping-pong?
A: Twenty-one

SCIENCE
Q: Which of these animals helps to pollinate flowers: an owl, a Mexican bat, or an alligator lizard?
A: A Mexican bat

- -

SCIENCE
Q: Groups of stars are a galaxy, groups of galaxies are a cluster, groups of clusters are a super-cluster. What is a group of super-clusters?
A: The universe

SPORTS
Q: In what year was women's soccer first an Olympic sport: 1976, 1986, or 1996?
A: 1996

OUR WORLD
Q: What is the first name of the lion-hearted English king who spent all but 6 months of his 10-year reign outside of England?
A: Richard (Richard I)

MEDIA
Q: In *The Wizard of Oz*, which direction did the Wicked Witch who melted come from?
A: West

NATURE
Q: True or false? It snows in Japan.
A: True

FAME
Q: Name the Clinton administration attorney general that shares her name with a Nevada gambling town.
A: Janet Reno

BLOCK 33

FAME
Q: What Jonathan Swift character got himself into a little trouble while traveling?
A: Gulliver

NATURE
Q: Which ocean laps the shores of Alaska, Greenland, and Russia?
A: The Arctic

MEDIA
Q: Which continent received proceeds from the song "We Are the World"?
A: Africa

OUR WORLD
Q: What trio of ice cream flavors are the most popular in the U.S.?
A: Chocolate, vanilla, strawberry

SPORTS
Q: How long is a regulation NBA basketball game?
A: 48 minutes (four 12-minute quarters)

SCIENCE
Q: Which of these particles carries a positive electrical charge: an electron, a neutron, or a proton?
A: A proton

- -

SCIENCE
Q: What four human body parts are most often mentioned in songs?
A: Eyes, hands, lips, and heart

SPORTS
Q: An Olympic javelin tip is always made of what metal?
A: Steel

OUR WORLD
Q: The people of what Caribbean island, known for its spiced rum, salsa, and sugar cane production, have U.S. passports?
A: Puerto Rico

MEDIA
Q: Where was Bob Dylan's answer "blowin'"?
A: In the wind

NATURE
Q: True or false? Bald eagles are bald.
A: False (They get their name from the Old English word for white, "balde.")

FAME
Q: What supermodel's real name is Eleanor Gow and is known as "The Body" in the business?
A: Elle Macpherson

BLOCK 34

BLOCK 35

FAME
Q: Minnesota was put on the map when this "Body" was put into the governor's office. Name the "Man."
A: Jesse Ventura

NATURE
Q: The cotton gin, invented by Eli Whitney in 1793, revolutionized the U.S. cotton industry. What did it remove from cotton?
A: Cotton seeds

MEDIA
Q: Name two of the three U.S. states that have served as titles for James Michener's sprawling epic novels.
A: Alaska, Hawaii, Texas

OUR WORLD
Q: What all-important U.S. legal document begins: "We, the people of the United States, in order to form a more perfect Union…"?
A: The Constitution

SPORTS
Q: Which event lasts longer: the Boston Marathon or an average professional baseball game?
A: The Boston Marathon

SCIENCE
Q: Which nebula could have appeared in the bed of a studio executive in *The Godfather*?
A: The Horsehead Nebula

• •

SCIENCE
Q: Which of these drugs is made from a fungus mold: aspirin, penicillin, or cortisone?
A: Penicillin

SPORTS
Q: True or false? Skateboarding was invented by California surfers who were frustrated by bad waves.
A: True

OUR WORLD
Q: What is the smallest U.S. coin—based on size, not worth?
A: Dime

MEDIA
Q: What was the high-ranking name of Bo and Luke's car in the TV show *Dukes of Hazzard*?
A: The General Lee

NATURE
Q: Name one of the four things a volcano can spew when it erupts.
A: Crystals, ash, gas, or lava

FAME
Q: What famous political theorist shares his last name with a family that left its "marks" on comedy?
A: Karl Marx (The Marx Brothers)

BLOCK 36

BLOCK 37

FAME
Q: In Henry Wadsworth Longfellow's poem about a little girl, where is her little curl?
A: Right in the middle of her forehead

NATURE
Q: True or false? Killer bees were imported to South America from Africa in the 1950's and have been slowly migrating northward ever since.
A: True

MEDIA
Q: In *Dumb and Dumber*, what expressive actor rides a scooter to Aspen, Colorado?
A: Jim Carrey

OUR WORLD
Q: Which country borders the most other countries?
A: China (16)

SPORTS
Q: Name two of the four most common types of golf clubs.
A: Driver, iron, putter, and wedge

SCIENCE
Q: Sigourney Weaver portrayed which dedicated zoologist in the 1988 film *Gorillas in the Mist*?
A: Dian Fossey

• •

SCIENCE
Q: True or false? Neptune is sometimes farther from the Sun than Pluto is from the Sun.
A: True

SPORTS
Q: Talented college player Dave Winfield was drafted for professional basketball, football, and baseball—which sport did he choose?
A: Baseball

OUR WORLD
Q: What vodka-rich country spans the largest number of time zones?
A: Russia

MEDIA
Q: True or false? Comedic actors Joan and John Cusack are cousins.
A: False (They're brother and sister.)

NATURE
Q: How many carats is pure gold: 18, 24, or 28?
A: 24 carats

FAME
Q: Which suave hero likes his martinis shaken and not stirred, and fights Dr. No and sharks, among other villains?
A: James Bond

BLOCK 38

Round 4

BLOCK 1

FAME
Q: What British scientist and all around do-gooder spent time in Tanzania and at Stanford's Jasper Ridge researching primates?
A: Jane Goodall

NATURE
Q: What flowering shrub got its name from the way insects sucked its golden nectar?
A: Honeysuckle

MEDIA
Q: What legendary rock and roll group's first album showed the explosion of the Hindenburg on its cover?
A: Led Zeppelin

OUR WORLD
Q: Which continent was once a penal colony and hosted the 2000 Olympic games?
A: Australia

SPORTS
Q: What is the world's most traveled professional sports trophy?
A: The Stanley Cup (Each player on the winning team is allowed to take it home for a few days.)

SCIENCE
Q: True or false? Air bubbles in the center of a hair shaft cause hair to turn gray.
A: True

- -

SCIENCE
Q: What measure of an object's resistance to force shares its name with a Roman Catholic church service?
A: Mass

SPORTS
Q: What sport are you playing if you have four walls, a ball, no paddles, and no racquet?
A: Handball

OUR WORLD
Q: What twentieth century president campaigned for change and was called The Bull Moose?
A: Teddy Roosevelt

MEDIA
Q: Mr. Hooper was the good-natured grocer on what famous street?
A: *Sesame Street*

NATURE
Q: True or false? Shrimp use their legs to swim.
A: True

FAME
Q: Who is sure to have a lock on his gate after making billions with his Windows?
A: Bill Gates

BLOCK 2

BLOCK 3

FAME
Q: What silly British spy said: "Let me ask you a question, and be honest ... Do I make you horny?!"
A: Austin Powers

NATURE
Q: What plant's immature flower is served as a tenderhearted vegetable?
A: Artichoke

MEDIA
Q: Actor James Earl Jones was the voice behind what evil *Star Wars* space invader?
A: Darth Vader

OUR WORLD
Q: What country on the Iberian Peninsula did Generalissimo Francisco Franco rule from 1939 to 1975?
A: Spain

SPORTS
Q: Fenway Park's green monster is 37 feet tall and painted green. Is it the wall for left field, center field, or right field?
A: Left field

SCIENCE
Q: What instrument is used to measure air pressure?
A: A barometer

SCIENCE
Q: Which of these dinosaurs is believed to have had the largest brain: stegosaurus, tyrannosaurus rex, or triceratops?
A: Tyrannosaurus rex

SPORTS
Q: We call them the New York Knicks, but that is actually a nickname. What's the team's full name?
A: The New York Knickerbockers

OUR WORLD
Q: Which high U.S. court holds the most legal power?
A: The Supreme Court

MEDIA
Q: Pippi Longstocking's horse bears the same straightforward name as Dudley Do-Right's horse. What is it?
A: Horse

NATURE
Q: The acronym HOMES is a great help in remembering an important set of names. What group does the acronym help with?
A: The Great Lakes

FAME
Q: What daytime talk show host has recently followed in Oprah's footsteps by starting her own magazine?
A: Rosie O'Donnell

BLOCK 4

BLOCK 5

FAME
Q: What Stanford graduate banked his U.S. presidential salary and gave it to charity?
A: Herbert Hoover

NATURE
Q: What New York landmark is struck by lightning approximately 100 times a year?
A: The Empire State Building

MEDIA
Q: What rock-busting tool shares its name with the title of the first hit song from Peter Gabriel's album entitled *So*?
A: "Sledgehammer"

OUR WORLD
Q: What bird from New Zealand shares its four-letter name with a fruit?
A: The kiwi

SPORTS
Q: Which athlete became the first African-American player to win a major men's tennis championship in 1968 at the U.S. Open?
A: Arthur Ashe

SCIENCE
Q: Which planet is the "butt" of the largest number of jokes (usually involving circling Klingons)?
A: Uranus

• •

SCIENCE
Q: In the fifteenth century, Johann Gutenburg used moveable type for the first time in history. What was the first book he printed?
A: The Bible

SPORTS
Q: In baseball, is it better for a pitcher to have a high earned run average or a low one?
A: A low one (the fewer runs allowed the better)

OUR WORLD
Q: In what crowded island country, home to the bento box and Hello Kitty® are the rooftops of buildings sometimes used for amusement parks?
A: Japan

MEDIA
Q: What chivalrous chess piece is the only one that doesn't move in a straight line?
A: The knight (horse)

NATURE
Q: What type of non-flying bird could be an emperor or a king?
A: The penguin

FAME
Q: What director's reputation soared after making *Jerry Maguire* and *Almost Famous*?
A: Cameron Crowe

BLOCK 6

BLOCK 7

FAME
Q: What country music star toured with Tim McGraw and later promised to be faithful when she married him in 1996?
A: Faith Hill

NATURE
Q: How many oceans are on Earth: three, four, or five?
A: Four (Arctic, Atlantic, Indian, Pacific)

MEDIA
Q: The first host of *Saturday Night Live* shares his first name with a famous "Dubya." Who is he?
A: George Carlin

OUR WORLD
Q: What body of water would you cross if traveling from the island of Majorca to Monte Carlo?
A: The Mediterranean Sea

SPORTS
Q: Joe Namath led the Jets to the 1969 Super Bowl. His nickname is taken from a famous street in New York City. What is the street?
A: Broadway ("Broadway" Joe)

SCIENCE
Q: What twentieth century paleoanthropologist greatly advanced the study of human evolution by "leaking" his discoveries to the scientific community?
A: Louis Leakey

• •

SCIENCE
Q: In 1928, Otto Frederick Rohwedder revolutionized the ease of sandwich making with an invention that all great things are compared to. What was the invention?
A: Sliced bread

SPORTS
Q: NBA power forward Karl Malone's nickname suggested he could deliver on the court. What was his nickname?
A: The Mailman

OUR WORLD
Q: What towering Alaskan mountain, with peaks over 19,000 feet, has the highest summit in North America?
A: Mt. McKinley (Denali)

MEDIA
Q: How old is the oldest teenage daughter in *The Sound of Music*?
A: 16 going on 17

NATURE
Q: Of the roughly 250 known shark species, what percentage are a threat to humans: 10%, 50%, or 75%?
A: 10%

FAME
Q: What famous fictional Southern belle vowed she'd never be hungry again?
A: Scarlett O'Hara

BLOCK 8

BLOCK 9

FAME
Q: Name the brave warrior who was invincible except for one tender spot near his ankles.
A: Achilles

NATURE
Q: True or false? Winds that transport lightning bolts create the sound that we hear as thunder.
A: False (Thunder is the sound of the lightning discharging into the atmosphere.)

MEDIA
Q: What's the name of the family-owned motel where Norman works in Hitchcock's *Psycho*?
A: The Bates Motel

OUR WORLD
Q: What nineteenth century political party that sounds like a hairpiece was once led by Zachary Taylor?
A: The Whig Party

SPORTS
Q: Which has more regulation playing time: a football game, a basketball game, or a soccer game?
A: A soccer game

SCIENCE
Q: Are you more likely to run into a myoclonic jerk while sleeping, at a mall, or at a baseball game?
A: While sleeping (It's an involuntary muscle spasm.)

• •

SCIENCE
Q: How much time passes every time the Earth makes one complete revolution?
A: One day (23 hours and 56 minutes)

SPORTS
Q: What is the foul called in field hockey when the player with the ball turns his or her back on the opponent: blocking, obstruction, or illegal turn?
A: Obstruction

OUR WORLD
Q: Name the popular Gothic Paris landmark that features gargoyles, a rose window, and a name that can be translated as "our lady."
A: Notre Dame

MEDIA
Q: What family of instruments does the clarinet belong to?
A: Woodwind

NATURE
Q: What are woodpeckers looking for when they peck into the trunks of old trees?
A: Insects to eat

FAME
Q: What enduring rockstar is better known as "Mod Rod"?
A: Rod Stewart

BLOCK 10

BLOCK 11

FAME
Q: During his presidency, Abraham Lincoln earned how much in annual salary: $2,500, $25,000, or $100,000?
A: $25,000

NATURE
Q: What plant bulb is sometimes deep fried and served at fast food restaurants?
A: Onion

MEDIA
Q: If you wanted to go to a place in Boston "where everybody knows your name," where would you be headed?
A: Cheers

OUR WORLD
Q: What is the four-letter name of the European Union's new currency?
A: Euro

SPORTS
Q: How far apart are the bases on a regulation baseball diamond: 60 feet, 75 feet, or 90 feet?
A: 90 feet

SCIENCE
Q: True or false? A light object has more inertia than a heavy object.
A: False

• •

SCIENCE
Q: The creator of the computer mouse, Douglas Engelbart, also created a larger, foot-operated version that failed to sell. What was it called: a moose, a rat, or a guinea pig?
A: A rat

SPORTS
Q: A three-second violation occurs in basketball when a member of the offense spends more than three seconds in what important area of the court?
A: The foul lane

OUR WORLD
Q: What nineteenth century "revolution" marked the transition from hand-produced to machine-produced goods?
A: The Industrial Revolution

MEDIA
Q: What swinger starred with future president Ronald Reagan in the movie *Bedtime for Bonzo?*
A: A chimpanzee

NATURE
Q: What part of the woolly mammoth's body was much smaller than the elephant's?
A: The ears

FAME
Q: Which red-haired royal has shared her weight loss secrets with the world?
A: Sarah Ferguson, Duchess of York

BLOCK 12

BLOCK 13

FAME
Q: What Michael Jackson hit features a rap by horror-film veteran Vincent Price?
A: "Thriller"

NATURE
Q: What percentage of Earth's water supply is fresh water available for direct human use: less than 1%, 25%, or 40%?
A: Less than 1%

MEDIA
Q: According to the title of F. Scott Fitzgerald's most famous book, what adjective describes Jay Gatsby?
A: Great (*The Great Gatsby*)

OUR WORLD
Q: Which Canadian province boasts killer skiing at Whistler, among other resorts?
A: British Columbia

SPORTS
Q: What college bowl game is called the "Granddaddy of Them All,®" and shares its name with a famous New Year's Day parade?
A: The Rose Bowl

SCIENCE
Q: Did plant-eating dinosaurs eat grass?
A: No, dinosaurs were extinct before grasses evolved

• •

SCIENCE
A: True
Q: True or false? An electric eel can give off enough current to light a light bulb.

SPORTS
A: The 1960s (1960)
Q: The first televised Olympic Games were in what decade?

OUR WORLD
A: Rome
Q: At 42 degrees north latitude, California's northern boundary runs through what Italian city?

MEDIA
A: Detroit
Q: What auto city is the home of Motown Record's original recording studio?

NATURE
A: True
Q: True or false? Most fish sleep.

FAME
A: The Philippines
January 2001?
Q: Gloria Macapagal Arroyo became president of what island nation country in

BLOCK 14

BLOCK 15

FAME
Q: Name the singer who worked *9 to 5* and has written over 3,000 songs.
A: Dolly Parton

NATURE
Q: From Japanese, "tsunami" is another commonly-used word for what?
A: A tidal wave

MEDIA
Q: What color is superhero Green Lantern helpless against?
A: Yellow

OUR WORLD
Q: What valuable black commodity do the countries of OPEC export?
A: Oil

SPORTS
Q: The Olympic motto is "Citius—altius—fortius." Give the English translation for one of these words.
A: Faster—higher—stronger

SCIENCE
Q: Which weighs more: salt water or fresh water?
A: Salt water

- -

SCIENCE
Q: Roger Sperry earned a Nobel Prize in 1981 for his work on the two hemispheres of what organ in the body?
A: The brain

SPORTS
Q: In 1990, which tennis powerhouse won a record ninth Wimbledon championship?
A: Martina Navratilova

OUR WORLD
Q: Thanks to a constitutional amendment, what's the maximum number of consecutive terms a U.S. president can serve?
A: Two

MEDIA
Q: Name the heavenly drummer of The Who.
A: Keith Moon

NATURE
Q: Which slow-moving mollusk has a kind of yellow fruit as its first name?
A: The banana slug

FAME
Q: It's not unusual to confuse Henry Fielding's eighteenth century hero with a legendary twentieth century lounge lizard. What name do they share?
A: Tom Jones

BLOCK 16

BLOCK 17

FAME
Q: What light-hearted character did Audrey Hepburn portray in the classic film, *Breakfast At Tiffany's*?
A: Holly Golightly

NATURE
Q: What sunny U.S. state contains the spot that gets the most rainy days per year?
A: Hawaii (Mt. Waialeale—up to 350 days per year)

MEDIA
Q: What "Science Guy" hosts a kid's show that rhymes with his nickname?
A: Bill Nye

OUR WORLD
Q: What adventurous two-man team is well known for exploring the northwestern U.S. in 1804?
A: Lewis and Clark

SPORTS
Q: What NHL player has scored the most playoff goals?
A: Wayne Gretzky (122)

SCIENCE
Q: During what year did Neil Armstrong take his historic walk on the moon?
A: 1969

SCIENCE
Q: What popular metal weighs down piggy banks and turns from reddish-brown to green when it gets old?
A: Copper

SPORTS
Q: What was the name of the scandal surrounding the 1919 World Series, in which Chicago White Sox players were bribed to throw the game?
A: The Black Sox scandal

OUR WORLD
Q: Did the Boxer Rebellion take place in California, China, or Thailand?
A: China

MEDIA
Q: What heavenly TV-based movie of 2000 features three undercover detectives?
A: *Charlie's Angles*

NATURE
Q: True or false? Tortoises and turtles do not have teeth.
A: True

FAME
Q: Who wrote the tragic play *The Death of a Salesman*: David Mamet or Arthur Miller?
A: Arthur Miller

BLOCK 18

BLOCK 19

FAME
Q: Evita Peron was the proud wife of the president of what South American country?
A: Argentina

NATURE
Q: Is amber made from fossilized tree resin, sedimentary rock, or petrified beehives?
A: Fossilized tree resin

MEDIA
Q: According to author Ken Kesey, how many flew over the cuckoo's nest?
A: One

OUR WORLD
Q: Name one country that borders Thailand.
A: Burma/Myanmar, Malaysia, Laos, or Cambodia

SPORTS
Q: Which can go fastest: a dragster, a stock car, or an Indy car?
A: A dragster

SCIENCE
Q: In 1854, Elias Howe sued Isaac Singer for patent infringement. What machine did Singer create and sell?
A: The sewing machine

- -

SCIENCE
Q: Over which Pole does the aurora borealis appear?
A: The North Pole

SPORTS
Q: In basketball, who is the only person who can call a timeout if his/her team is not in control of the ball?
A: The head coach

OUR WORLD
Q: What's the female equivalent of a Cub Scout that sounds like a delicious treat?
A: A Brownie

MEDIA
Q: What Scottish stud portrayed James Bond in the 1960s, 1970s, and 1980s?
A: Sean Connery

NATURE
Q: Roughly how many volcanoes, including those underwater, are currently active on Earth: 150, 350, or 850?
A: 850

FAME
Q: What nineteenth century emancipator died sitting in one of the best seats in the house at the Ford Theater?
A: Abraham Lincoln

BLOCK 20

BLOCK 21

FAME
Q: What author wrote the *New York Times* bestseller *The Joy Luck Club* and sounds like she's been in the sun?
A: Amy Tan

NATURE
Q: Blue whales can weigh up to 135 tons. Roughly how many elephants does it take to equal the weight of one blue whale: 10, 15, or 20?
A: 20

MEDIA
Q: What is the whimsical title of Ian Fleming's novel about a magical car?
A: *Chitty Chitty Bang Bang*

OUR WORLD
Q: Since 1995, the largest number of legal immigrants to the U.S. have come from what country?
A: Mexico

SPORTS
Q: What U.S. Olympic swimmer won an amazing seven gold medals, posting world records in every event he participated in?
A: Mark Spitz

SCIENCE
Q: Which of these foods is highest in protein: spinach, beans, or apples?
A: Beans

· ·

SCIENCE
Q: In which physical state is most matter heaviest: solid, liquid, or gas?
A: Solid

SPORTS
Q: True or false? Ping-pong was named because of the sounds the ball makes when it hits the paddle and the table.
A: True

OUR WORLD
Q: What is the last U.S. bank holiday of each year?
A: Christmas

MEDIA
Q: What southern city, named for an ancient Egyptian city, contains the home of Elvis Presley?
A: Memphis

NATURE
Q: What is the name of the grassland that the nomadic peoples of Central Eurasia have been walking along since ancient times?
A: The steppe

FAME
Q: What celebrity won Best Actress in a movie about a famous Virginia and was once married to a Senator from Virginia?
A: Elizabeth Taylor

BLOCK 22

BLOCK 23

FAME
Q: What acclaimed director is known as an unofficial New York Knick and launched his career with *She's Gotta Have It* in 1986?
A: Spike Lee

NATURE
Q: What large Mexican plant is closely associated with the Christmas season?
A: The poinsettia

MEDIA
Q: *All in the Family's* Archie and Edith have a surname that sounds like an army dwelling. What is it?
A: Bunker

OUR WORLD
Q: On a globe, do latitude lines run east and west, or north and south?
A: East and west

SPORTS
Q: Which sisters teamed up and won both a Wimbledon championship and Olympic gold medals in 2000?
A: The Williams Sisters (Venus and Serena)

SCIENCE
Q: Is the sun directly overhead in the morning, at midday, or in the evening?
A: At midday

• •

SCIENCE
Q: True or false? The same person invented both the telegraph and Morse code.
A: True (Samuel Morse)

SPORTS
Q: Which of these sports does not have an infield: baseball, football, or horse racing?
A: Football

OUR WORLD
Q: What U.S. state has the longest coastline?
A: Alaska

MEDIA
Q: What high-flying Irish rock group shares its name with a U.S. spy plane?
A: U2

NATURE
Q: Which do not live in colonies: ants, termites, or grasshoppers?
A: Grasshoppers

FAME
Q: What actor played himself as a real head case in a 1999 film directed by Spike Jonze?
A: John Malkovich (*Being John Malkovich*)

BLOCK 24

BLOCK 25

FAME
Q: What was the wildly equestrian name of one chief of the Oglala Sioux?
A: Crazy Horse

NATURE
Q: In what country does South America's Amazon River flow into the Atlantic Ocean?
A: Brazil

MEDIA
Q: Does the orchestra play an overture at the beginning, middle, or end of an opera?
A: Beginning

OUR WORLD
Q: How many senators does Nevada elect to Congress: two, three, or five?
A: Two

SPORTS
Q: What word in chess literally translates to "The king is dead."?
A: Checkmate

SCIENCE
Q: True or false? Insulin works to reduce the level of sugar in the blood.
A: True

SCIENCE
Q: Many scientists believe that our universe formed out of a massive explosion. What is the working name of this theory?
A: The Big Bang Theory

SPORTS
Q: True or false? Professional female golfers hit golf balls farther than professional baseball players hit home runs.
A: True

OUR WORLD
Q: The Arabian Peninsula is the world's largest. On what continent is it located?
A: Asia

MEDIA
Q: Name the two-letter TV series about a hospital that became a big hit in the mid-1990s.
A: ER

NATURE
Q: Roughly how many earthquakes occur around the world each year: 1000, 100,000 or 1,000,000?
A: 1,000,000

FAME
Q: In what classic Martin Scorsese film was Robert De Niro driven to ask himself, "You talkin' to me? You talkin' to me?"
A: *Taxi Driver*

BLOCK 26

BLOCK 27

FAME
Q: What actor was born Carlos Irwin Estevez but is better known by his slick stage name?
A: Charlie Sheen

NATURE
Q: Name the U.S. state that boasts the world's longest island chain.
A: Hawaii

MEDIA
Q: Name the only one of the seven dwarfs who doesn't have a beard.
A: Dopey

OUR WORLD
Q: Which is larger: Ceylon or Sri Lanka?
A: Neither! (Ceylon officially changed its name to Sri Lanka in 1972.)

SPORTS
Q: His real name is Edson Arantes do Nascimento, but most people know this soccer great by what nickname?
A: Pele

SCIENCE
Q: When ice thaws do its molecules expand or contract?
A: They contract

SCIENCE
Q: What process transforms a tadpole into a frog?
A: Metamorphosis

SPORTS
Q: In what decade did Doug Williams become the first African-American to start as a quarterback in a Super Bowl?
A: 1980s (1988)

OUR WORLD
Q: What war started with shots fired on Fort Sumter in 1861?
A: The Civil War

MEDIA
Q: What dark poem by Edgar Allen Poe starts out, "Once upon a midnight dreary…"?
A: The Raven

NATURE
Q: Is a baby pigeon called a squab, a gosling, or a poult?
A: A squab

FAME
Q: What champ refused to join the U.S. army on religious grounds in 1967 and was said to "float like a butterfly and sting like a bee"?
A: Muhammad Ali

BLOCK 28

BLOCK 29

FAME
Q: What's the most exotic animal ever owned by the British royal family: Vietnamese Pot-Bellied pigs, Haitian hamsters, or Pygmy hippopotami?
A: Pygmy hippopotami (Presented to The Duke of Edinburgh by the President of Liberia in 1961.)

NATURE
Q: True or false? Cold-blooded animals maintain a constant internal body temperature.
A: False (Their body temperature adjusts to their surroundings)

MEDIA
Q: Woodstock II was in 1994. What year was the original concert held?
A: 1969

OUR WORLD
Q: Boasting a majestic waterfront opera house, which Australian city was also the site of the 2000 Olympics?
A: Sydney

SPORTS
Q: Tennis was excluded from the Olympics from 1928 until what year: 1948, 1968, or 1988?
A: 1988

SCIENCE
Q: Is acid rain created by spilling acid, burning fossil fuels, or testing nuclear bombs?
A: Burning fossil fuels

• •

SCIENCE
Q: What husband-and-wife team discovered radium in 1898?
A: Pierre and Marie Curie

SPORTS
Q: How many outs are in a nine-inning baseball game won by the visiting team?
A: 54

OUR WORLD
Q: What is a shallow body of salt water that shares its name with a 1980 Brooke Shields movie?
A: Lagoon (*Blue Lagoon*)

MEDIA
Q: According to the title of 1969's Best Picture, what hour describes cowboy Joe Buck?
A: Midnight (*Midnight Cowboy*)

NATURE
Q: What fruit do you need to produce ketchup?
A: Tomato

FAME
Q: When he won an Academy Award® for his role as a priest in *Going My Way*, who said "I couldn't be more surprised if I won the Kentucky Derby?"
A: Bing Crosby

BLOCK 30

BLOCK 31

FAME
Q: Which president, rumored to have had wooden teeth, had his horses' teeth brushed daily?
A: George Washington

NATURE
Q: What type of reef is separated from land by a lagoon?
A: A barrier reef

MEDIA
Q: Henrietta Hippo made it big on what children's TV show: *The New Zoo Review*, *Captain Kangaroo*, or *The Banana Splits*?
A: *The New Zoo Review*

OUR WORLD
Q: What country built the Panama Canal?
A: The U.S.

SPORTS
Q: If a horse wins the Kentucky Derby, the Belmont Stakes, and the Preakness in one year, what is this royal accomplishment known as?
A: The Triple Crown

SCIENCE
Q: The microscope is named from the Greek word micros, meaning "small." What instrument is named from the Greek word meaning "far off"?
A: The telescope

* *

SCIENCE
Q: What substance in green plants gives them their green color: chlorophyll, chloroform, or Coloforms®?
A: Chlorophyll

SPORTS
Q: True or false? The LA Lakers were originally based in Minneapolis.
A: True

OUR WORLD
Q: Which of these is worth more: a bucket full of nickels or the same bucket half full of dimes?
A: A bucket half full of dimes

MEDIA
Q: What Anne Rice novel was made into a movie starring Tom Cruise?
A: *Interview with a Vampire*

NATURE
Q: What is the plural of "moose"?
A: Moose

FAME
Q: This fictional Scandinavian redhead sports a silly hairstyle and never wears matching socks. Who is she?
A: Pippi Longstocking

BLOCK 32

BLOCK 33

FAME
Q: In 1993, *Time* magazine named four men "Men of the Year" in a special "Peacemakers" issue. Name one of the two who hailed from the Middle East.
A: Yasser Arafat and Yitzhak Rabin

NATURE
Q: What bristly purple plant is also known as the national emblem of Scotland?
A: Thistle

MEDIA
Q: What singing group led the "British Invasion"?
A: The Beatles

OUR WORLD
Q: What powerful but now defunct nation, ruled by Frederick the Great, led the formation of the German empire?
A: Prussia

SPORTS
Q: What is the official weight of the Olympic men's shot put: 6 pounds, 16 pounds, or 60 pounds?
A: 16 pounds

SCIENCE
Q: The USSR's Soyuz spacecraft formed a famous union in 1975. Which U.S. spacecraft did it dock with: Apollo, Skylab, or Gemini?
A: Apollo

SCIENCE
Q: Is ozone a form of oxygen, hydrogen, or helium?
A: Oxygen

SPORTS
Q: In boxing, which is heavier: a lightweight or a flyweight?
A: A lightweight

OUR WORLD
Q: How many oceans do U.S. states touch?
A: Three (Atlantic, Pacific, Arctic)

MEDIA
Q: Which women's magazine sounds like a trendy cocktail and was once run by Helen Gurley Brown?
A: *Cosmopolitan*

NATURE
Q: True or false? In terms of surface area covered, there is more water in the oceans than in the atmosphere.
A: False

FAME
Q: What rising Latina pop star was shot to death by the president of her own fan club and was portrayed by Jennifer Lopez in a 1997 movie?
A: Selena

BLOCK 34

BLOCK 35

FAME
Q: What notoriously destructive couple was immortalized on film by Gary Oldman and Chloe Webb?
A: Sid Vicious and Nancy Spungen

NATURE
Q: Does the Yukon River flow into the Arctic Ocean, the Bering Sea, or the Caspian Sea?
A: The Bering Sea

MEDIA
Q: Who is the captain who unrelentingly pursues Moby Dick, the great white whale?
A: Ahab

OUR WORLD
Q: Which military branch has sustained the most casualties in every major U.S. war?
A: The Army

SPORTS
Q: To compete as a boxing heavyweight, you must tip the scales at what weight or above?
A: 190 pounds

SCIENCE
Q: To determine whether a rock on the moon is bigger than a rock on Earth, should you ask for their weights or their masses?
A: Masses

• •

SCIENCE
Q: The U.S.'s Viking probe was the first spacecraft to reach Mars. During which decade did Viking reach Mars?
A: The 1970s (1976)

SPORTS
Q: In 1956, the Summer Olympic Games in Melbourne, Australia were held in November and December. Why?
A: The Southern Hemisphere has a reversal of seasons.

OUR WORLD
Q: Frank Sinatra crooned about which two highly populated U.S. cities?
A: New York and Chicago

MEDIA
Q: True or false? All of the clocks in the movie *Pulp Fiction* are stuck at 4:20.
A: True

NATURE
Q: The names for male, female, and baby geese all start with what letter of the alphabet?
A: G (gander, goose, gosling)

FAME
Q: Which of the following figures was not one of Christ's original disciples: Thomas, Urkel, or James?
A: Urkel

BLOCK 36

• • • • • • • • • • • • • • • • • • • 84 • • • • • • • • • • • • • • • • • • •

BLOCK 37

FAME
Q: What husband and wife team founded a well-known women's cosmetics line in New York City in 1946?
A: Estée and Joseph Lauder (Estée Lauder)

NATURE
Q: What plant named for a jungle cat also shares its name with a character from *Peter Pan*?
A: The tiger lily

MEDIA
Q: Jed Clampett was shootin' at some food when he struck oil. Name two of the three names for oil in his TV theme song.
A: Bubblin' crude, black gold, Texas tea

OUR WORLD
Q: What color is the square that Lenin's Tomb sits on?
A: Red

SPORTS
Q: In 1900, the first American athlete won an Olympic medal. What was her sport?
A: Golf (Margaret Abbott)

SCIENCE
Q: Which of these subjects do paleontologists study: plants and animals of long ago, minerals, or skin diseases?
A: Plants and animals of long ago

• •

SCIENCE
Q: Which of these dinosaurs was closest in weight to a modern elephant (about seven tons): allosaurus, stegosaurus, or triceratops?
A: Triceratops

SPORTS
Q: With 6,082 yards, Tony Dorsett set what collegiate record from 1973 to 1976?
A: Career rushing in college football

OUR WORLD
Q: Which one of the Great Lakes shares its name with a U.S. state?
A: Lake Michigan

MEDIA
Q: According to the title of a William Faulkner novel, which month has light in it?
A: August (*Light in August*)

NATURE
Q: Generally recognized as the worst natural disaster of the twentieth century, a terrible cyclone and flood in 1970 claimed a half million casualties in what small neighbor of India?
A: Bangladesh

FAME
Q: How many pigs were used to produce the film Babe: 6, 60, or 600?
A: 60

BLOCK 38

Round 5

FAME
Q: Which British royal was dubbed the "Queen of Hearts," even though she was merely a princess?
A: Princess Diana

NATURE
Q: Which African mammal has a name that is part dermatological flaw and part large pig?
A: The warthog

MEDIA
Q: Give the four-word name of the boy whose "name is my name too," according to a popular song.
A: John Jacob Jingleheimer Schmidt

OUR WORLD
Q: What thriving Indian metropolis shares its name with a plaid fabric?
A: Madras, India

SPORTS
Q: What interrupted the 1989 World Series between the San Francisco Giants and the Oakland A's?
A: An earthquake

SCIENCE
Q: What did innovative butcher Charles Feltman open in Coney Island in 1871?
A: The first hot dog stand

• •

SCIENCE
Q: On a sunny day, will your shadow be longest in the morning, at midday, or at night?
A: In the morning

SPORTS
Q: From 1969 to 1977, the NCAA banned what now-familiar basketball move?
A: The slam-dunk

OUR WORLD
Q: Which of these great religious thinkers sought enlightenment while sitting under a tree: Buddha, Jesus, or Moses?
A: Buddha

MEDIA
Q: Name the type of legume that George Washington Carver and Charles Schulz made famous.
A: Peanuts

NATURE
Q: True or false? Cats' taste buds cannot distinguish "sweet."
A: True

FAME
Q: What African-American civil rights activist took action—and a seat—in 1955 in Montgomery, Alabama?
A: Rosa Parks

FAME
Q: What former beauty queen committed suicide with an asp's bite?
A: Cleopatra, queen of Egypt

NATURE
Q: What country claims the second largest geographic area in the world, after Russia?
A: Canada

MEDIA
Q: Matthew Broderick plays a tricky truant in what popular 1986 John Hughes flick?
A: *Ferris Bueller's Day Off*

OUR WORLD
Q: Cream cheese, cheddar, Colby, and Gruyère boast the most what, compared to other kinds of cheese?
A: Fat

SPORTS
Q: This first baseman's name is now synonymous with a serious illness, but he was known as the "Iron Horse" while he played. Who is he?
A: Lou Gehrig

SCIENCE
Q: What minor planets share their name with a popular 1980s video game?
A: Asteroids

- -

SCIENCE
Q: What scientific process is at work when a starfish loses an arm and grows a new one?
A: Regeneration

SPORTS
Q: What is the rhyming name of a pre-game strategy session, even if there's no blackboard nearby?
A: Chalk talk

OUR WORLD
Q: Toga-clad citizens of what two ancient cities fought in the Peloponnesian War?
A: Athens and Sparta

MEDIA
Q: According to the upbeat song from *Snow White and the Seven Dwarfs*, what does Snow White do while she works?
A: Whistle ("Whistle While You Work")

NATURE
Q: Found mostly along the California coast, which appropriately named sea mammal's males usually grow to about 21 feet long and 7,500 pounds?
A: The elephant seal

FAME
Q: What Green Bay Packers quarterback led his team to a 1997 Super Bowl victory and played a bit part in the movie *There's Something About Mary?*
A: Brett Favre

BLOCK 5

FAME
Q: What late congressman admitted loving Chastity…and her mother, too?
A: Sonny Bono

NATURE
Q: What flower is the namesake of a Duck, a Duke, and a driven Miss?
A: Daisy

MEDIA
Q: Which 1950s TV program left it to a boy named after an animal and was the first to show a toilet on television?
A: *Leave it to Beaver*

OUR WORLD
Q: Placed in alphabetical order, what two continents come first?
A: Africa, Antarctica

SPORTS
Q: Helpful John Stockton holds the NBA record for what, with over 12,000 in his career?
A: Assists

SCIENCE
Q: Think back: What does the "M" in "CD-ROM" stand for?
A: Memory

• •

SCIENCE
Q: What prolific inventor created bifocals in the 1780s?
A: Ben Franklin

SPORTS
Q: In which of these sports does a fullback play on offense: football, rugby or soccer?
A: Football

OUR WORLD
Q: The Suez Canal can be found in what North African country, home to the Great Pyramids?
A: Egypt

MEDIA
Q: What singing trio had an un-bee-lievable number of songs on the *Saturday Night Fever* soundtrack?
A: Bee Gees

NATURE
Q: Which elephant is larger: the African or the Indian elephant?
A: African elephant

FAME
Q: What prolific author wrote the novella upon which the 1994 film *The Shawshank Redemption* was based?
A: Stephen King

BLOCK 6

GAME OF KNOWLEDGE

BLOCK 7

FAME
Q: What First Lady is a former fashion model, a dancer, and a recovering alcoholic?
A: Betty Ford

NATURE
Q: Which are born hairless, blind, and helpless: rabbits or hares?
A: Rabbits

MEDIA
Q: What group of comic book superheroes includes Mr. Fantastic, Human Torch, Invisible Woman, and the Thing?
A: The Fantastic Four

OUR WORLD
Q: Which of these great ancient civilizations flourished first: Egyptian, Roman, or Greek?
A: Egyptian

SPORTS
Q: The Los Angeles Sparks belong to what women's sporting league?
A: The Women's National Basketball Association (WNBA)

SCIENCE
Q: What scientist wrote the 1988 bestseller *A Brief History of Time* and is often thought of as the greatest mind in physics since Albert Einstein?
A: Stephen Hawking

SCIENCE
Q: True or false? Most sleep researchers believe that humans dream for more than 50% of their time asleep.
A: False (no more than 25%)

SPORTS
Q: In 1915, which president of the United States became the first to attend a World Series game?
A: Woodrow Wilson

OUR WORLD
Q: What English settlement contains a common man's name and was founded in 1607 in present-day Virginia?
A: Jamestown

MEDIA
Q: What Humphrey Bogart movie hinged on a quest for an object lost by the Knights Templar of Malta?
A: *The Maltese Falcon*

NATURE
Q: Name the fracture between rocks that can be blamed for an earthquake.
A: A fault

FAME
Q: What jiggly food product is Bill Cosby associated with?
A: Jell-O®

BLOCK 8

BLOCK 9

FAME
Q: Name the media mogul who once won the America's Cup and is the founder of the Goodwill Games.
A: Ted Turner

NATURE
Q: When the barometer falls, can we expect good weather or bad weather?
A: Bad weather

MEDIA
Q: What famous novel by Fyodor Dostoyevsky might make you think twice about committing a crime?
A: *Crime and Punishment*

OUR WORLD
Q: What kind of animals are part of the team in the Iditarod race?
A: Dogs (The Iditarod is a dogsledding race)

SPORTS
Q: The first World Cup was won by Uruguay in what year: 1910, 1930, or 1950?
A: 1930

SCIENCE
Q: Name the scale that tells you whether a substance is an acid or a base.
A: The pH scale

. . . .

SCIENCE
Q: Which of these areas of physics describes the study of matter at rest: dynamics, kinematics, or statics?
A: Statics

SPORTS
Q: How many minutes is a major penalty in ice hockey?
A: Five

OUR WORLD
Q: Who served as Queen of Scots and then ascended the throne of England: Mary, Anne, or Victoria?
A: Mary

MEDIA
Q: What 1970s European musical group was so popular that the stage musical *Mamma Mia* was based entirely on its songs?
A: ABBA

NATURE
Q: Which of these comes from a plant: a wool sweater, blue jeans, or a silk scarf?
A: Blue jeans (the cotton plant)

FAME
Q: Who was the first American president to visit Hanoi following the Vietnam War?
A: President Clinton

BLOCK 10

BLOCK 11

FAME	Q: What famous rock star earned his nickname by buzzing around in a black-and-yellow striped shirt? A: Sting (Gordon Sumner)
NATURE	Q: The world's highest waterfall, Angel Falls, which gets awfully close to heaven at over 2,500 feet, is located in what South American country? A: Venezuela
MEDIA	Q: In *Guys & Dolls*, Marlon Brando sings about luck. He pictures luck as what? A: A lady ("Luck Be a Lady")
OUR WORLD	Q: Puerto Rican pop diva J. Lo hails from which New York City borough? A: The Bronx (Jennifer Lopez)
SPORTS	Q: What are the three elements of baseball's Triple Crown? A: Home runs, batting average, and RBI's (runs batted in)
SCIENCE	Q: Who theorized that an accidental slip of the tongue actually reveals something meaningful from the "dynamic unconscious"? A: Sigmund Freud

• •

SCIENCE	Q: Which of these marine animals is not an invertebrate: a lobster, a seal, or a squid? A: A seal
SPORTS	Q: In baseball, what kind of game is it when one team does not score? A: A shut out
OUR WORLD	Q: The resolution of the Tilden-Hayes debate in 1876 led to Rutherford B. Hayes' presidency. The debate, much like the Gore-Bush election debacle, concerned one crucial election fact. What was it? A: Who won the election
MEDIA	Q: What four-letter word ends most prayers and ends the Bible, too? A: Amen
NATURE	Q: What wise plant is used as a spice and lends its name to a brush? A: Sage
FAME	Q: True or false? The Beatles and Elvis never met. A: False (They met once at Elvis' Bel Air, California home in 1965.)

BLOCK 12

BLOCK 13

FAME
Q: Famous for his "Twist," the nickname of what 1950s singer hints at his tubby physique?
A: Chubby Checker

NATURE
Q: What endangered animal has been the symbol for the World Wildlife Fund since 1962?
A: A giant panda

MEDIA
Q: Arnold Schwarzenegger plays a cyborg sent from the future to end lives in what 1984 movie?
A: *The Terminator*

OUR WORLD
Q: What country has the most English-speaking inhabitants outside the U.S.?
A: The UK

SPORTS
Q: The Olympic torch always starts its journey in what city?
A: Olympia, Greece

SCIENCE
Q: True or false? The moon orbits Earth from west to east.
A: True

. . . .

SCIENCE
Q: Which of these dinosaurs had three horns: triceratops, ankylosaurus, or apatosaurus?
A: Triceratops

SPORTS
Q: True or false? Baseball is North America's oldest team sport.
A: False (Lacrosse has been played by Native Americans since the 1400s.)

OUR WORLD
Q: What U.S. state consists of two separate landmasses connected by the Mackinac Bridge?
A: Michigan

MEDIA
Q: In the TV sit-com *The Wonder Years*, what child actor with a tough-sounding last name played Kevin Arnold?
A: Fred Savage

NATURE
Q: The Andes Mountains extend the entire length of what continent?
A: South America

FAME
Q: What famous red head has an Australian accent but was actually born in Honolulu, Hawaii in 1967?
A: Nicole Kidman

BLOCK 14

BLOCK 15

FAME
Q: What actor said, "Mrs. Robinson, do you think we could say a few words to each other first this time?"
A: Dustin Hoffman in *The Graduate*

NATURE
Q: Prayers of what insect won't help the male species—who end up as a meal after mating?
A: The praying mantis

MEDIA
Q: True or false? The X-Men only include mutant men.
A: False

OUR WORLD
Q: Which of Congress' two legislative bodies has more members: the Senate or the House of Representatives?
A: The House of Representatives

SPORTS
Q: Widely regarded as the best soccer player of all time, Brazilian great Pele played what position: striker, midfielder, or defenseman?
A: Striker

SCIENCE
Q: What arrangement of chemical elements did Mendeleyev start?
A: The periodic table

• •

SCIENCE
Q: In 1953, who invented condensed milk: Gail Borden, John Carnation, or John Hershey?
A: Gail Borden

SPORTS
Q: What infamous switch-hitter shares his first name with a Disney character and once said, "If I had played my career hitting singles like Pete (Rose), I'd wear a dress"?
A: Mickey Mantle

OUR WORLD
Q: In 1821, Mexico was granted independence from what European country?
A: Spain

MEDIA
Q: According to the best selling book, if men are from Mars, where are women from?
A: Venus

NATURE
Q: True or false? North of the equator, Earth's gravity makes whirlpools spin counter-clockwise.
A: False (They spin clockwise.)

FAME
Q: What recording artist claims to have a seven-inch long tongue?
A: Gene Simmons of KISS

BLOCK 16

BLOCK 17

FAME
Q: Who won the Best Actor Oscar in 2001: Tom Hanks, Russell Crowe, or Benicio Del Toro?
A: Russell Crowe (for *Gladiator*)

NATURE
Q: The cacao's seeds are dried and ground to produce what tasty treat?
A: Chocolate

MEDIA
Q: What rock icon turned 50 in 1997 and glammed it up as Ziggy Stardust in the 1970s?
A: David Bowie

OUR WORLD
Q: What city in the Netherlands is home to the Van Gogh Museum?
A: Amsterdam

SPORTS
Q: What does NASCAR stand for?
A: National Association for Stock Car Auto Racing

SCIENCE
Q: True or false? A newborn chick can peck at its shell up to 1,000 times before it escapes.
A: True

• •

SCIENCE
Q: Roughly how often does Haley's Comet appear: every year, once in a blue moon, or about once every century?
A: About once every century (about every 76 years)

SPORTS
Q: Who duked it out on the tennis court in 1973's "Battle of the Sexes"?
A: Bobby Riggs and Billie Jean King (She won.)

OUR WORLD
Q: Aside from flowers, jewelry, and perfume, what is the most common gift for a sweetie on Valentine's Day?
A: Chocolate

MEDIA
Q: Which of Shakespeare's plays has the most words: *Othello, Romeo and Juliet,* or *Hamlet?*
A: *Hamlet*

NATURE
Q: Is coral an animal, a vegetable, or a mineral?
A: An animal (It's an invertebrate.)

FAME
Q: What world leader shortened her name after marrying Morris Myerson and served as Israel's Prime Minister from 1969–1974?
A: Golda Meir

BLOCK 18

BLOCK 19

FAME
Q: What stage name does actress Diane Hall, who played the lead in a 1977 Oscar® winning Woody Allen movie, go by?
A: Diane Keaton (*Annie Hall*)

NATURE
Q: Earth's circumference is roughly 25,000 miles. What's the farthest away from home you can be without leaving Earth's surface?
A: 12,500 miles

MEDIA
Q: What was Homer Simpson's new occupation in the episode where he changes his name to "Mr. Plow"?
A: Snow plow driver

OUR WORLD
Q: Medieval knights challenged enemies by throwing down a gauntlet. Is a gauntlet a glove, a scarf, or a knife?
A: A glove

SPORTS
Q: At 31.5 points per game, which NBA player holds the record for highest scoring average?
A: Michael Jordan

SCIENCE
Q: Do two magnets with the same polarity attract or repel each other?
A: Repel each other

- -

SCIENCE
Q: Is a plant or animal in the early stages of its development called a placenta, a neonate, or an embryo?
A: An embryo

SPORTS
Q: True or false? When Mary Lou Retton won the all-around gold medal in Olympic gymnastics, she was only 4 feet 9 inches tall.
A: True

OUR WORLD
Q: What U.S. coastal state is the most visited by both international and domestic travelers?
A: California

MEDIA
Q: Name the devilish title of the devilish book that caused Salmon Rushdie to fear for his life.
A: *The Satanic Verses*

NATURE
Q: What is the name of the process plants use to synthesize the sun's light into the energy they need to grow?
A: Photosynthesis

FAME
Q: Which president used the song "Don't Stop Thinking About Tomorrow" by Fleetwood Mac as a theme for his inaugural ball?
A: Bill Clinton

BLOCK 20

BLOCK 21

FAME
Q: The film *Apocalypse Now* was narrated by the same man who now plays the president on TV's *West Wing*. Who is he?
A: Martin Sheen

NATURE
Q: Name the man-made body of water that both connects the Mediterranean and Red Sea and separates Asia from Africa.
A: The Suez Canal

MEDIA
Q: Which of these is the meaning of the musical term "crescendo": very soft, pause, or gradually becoming louder?
A: Gradually louder

OUR WORLD
Q: In what roaring decade was the first U.S. transcontinental airmail route established?
A: The 1920s

SPORTS
Q: What baseball team boasts winning the most Rookie of the Year Awards?
A: The Dodgers (Brooklyn and Los Angeles)

SCIENCE
Q: What inventor made it possible in 1876 for us to chat with friends miles away—and opened the door for intercoms, walkie-talkies, radio, and even the Internet?
A: Alexander Graham Bell, who invented the first telephone

• •

SCIENCE
Q: Name two of the four most consumed energy sources.
A: Petroleum, natural gas, coal, and nuclear

SPORTS
Q: In what sport do athletes learn the nelson, the cradle, and the hammerlock?
A: Wrestling

OUR WORLD
Q: Which U.S. war accounted for the highest number of non-battle deaths among U.S. soldiers?
A: The Civil War

MEDIA
Q: Desilu Productions was named for a husband and wife comedy team. Name the wife.
A: Lucille Ball

NATURE
Q: What member of the weasel family usually stomps its feet in warning before unleashing its most famous—and powerful—defense weapon?
A: The skunk

FAME
Q: What style of music from the West Indies shares its name with Jacques Cousteau's boat?
A: Calypso

BLOCK 22

BLOCK 23

FAME
Q: Name two of the four top-grossing movies released in the 1930s.
A: *Gone With the Wind, Snow White and the Seven Dwarfs, The Woman in Red,* and *The Wizard of Oz*

NATURE
Q: Which of these conditions is not aggravated by depletion of the ozone layer: acid rain, global warming, or skin cancer?
A: Acid rain

MEDIA
Q: In what year did Frank Capra direct Clark Gable and Claudette Colbert in *It Happened One Night*: 1924, 1934, or 1944?
A: 1934

OUR WORLD
Q: How many fingers are used in the Boy Scouts of America salute?
A: Three

SPORTS
Q: In what sport are both the thing you hit with and the thing you hit full of holes?
A: Badminton

SCIENCE
Q: What bone-building mineral found in milk is the most common mineral in the human body?
A: Calcium

- -

SCIENCE
Q: The planet that orbits the sun fastest gets its name from Roman mythology's winged messenger. Name the planet.
A: Mercury

SPORTS
Q: Who is the youngest player, and the only German, to win the men's singles at Wimbledon?
A: Boris Becker

OUR WORLD
Q: True or false? Taiwan is governed by the People's Republic of China.
A: False

MEDIA
Q: Who was first actor cast to play James Bond: Sean Connery, Roger Moore, or Ian Fleming?
A: Sean Connery

NATURE
Q: True or false? Tigers, like their domesticated housecat cousins, hate water.
A: False

FAME
Q: What beloved country boy took his performing name from Colorado's capital?
A: John Denver

BLOCK 24

BLOCK 25

FAME
Q: The canine hero of Jack London's *Call of the Wild* sounds like he might be worth a dollar. What is his name?
A: Buck

NATURE
Q: The first F5 tornado to hit the Oklahoma City metro area blew through in what year: 1990, 1995, or 1999?
A: 1999

MEDIA
Q: Which was invented first: the harpsichord or the piano?
A: The harpsichord (sixteenth century)

OUR WORLD
Q: What Italian explorer reached China in 1275 and has the same name as a game kids play in the pool?
A: Marco Polo

SPORTS
Q: Which college Division 1-A national championship is not decided by a tournament or playoff system: football, basketball, or wrestling?
A: Football

SCIENCE
Q: How many pounds does the largest meteorite on display in a museum weigh: 6,800, 68,000, or 680,000?
A: 68,000 pounds (It can be seen at the American Museum of Natural History in New York City.)

● ●

SCIENCE
Q: What hot topic does thermodynamics deal with: the effect of global warming on the planet or the transfer of heat to and from other forms of energy?
A: The transfer of heat

SPORTS
Q: In which sport does the participant reach the highest speed: bobsledding, downhill skiing, or the 100-meter dash?
A: Downhill skiing

OUR WORLD
Q: What four basic hues come in a standard four-pack of food coloring?
A: Red, blue, yellow, and green

MEDIA
Q: True or False? David Letterman's sidekick on the TV show *Late Night With David Letterman* is Phil Spector.
A: False (David Letterman's sidekick is Paul Shaffer.)

NATURE
Q: What landlocked country is bordered by Italy, France, Germany, Liechtenstein, and Austria?
A: Switzerland

FAME
Q: What actress is named after a Hindu goddess and recently signed a contract with Lancome?
A: Uma Thurman

BLOCK 26

BLOCK 27

FAME
Q: What actor with a presidential last name picked up a Golden Globe in *The Hurricane*?
A: Denzel Washington (for his portrayal of Rubin "Hurricane" Carter)

NATURE
Q: Which flower's name combines a hot continent with a color?
A: African violet

MEDIA
Q: What does Tom Sawyer whitewash in Mark Twain's *The Adventures of Tom Sawyer*?
A: A fence

OUR WORLD
Q: What does a white dove symbolize?
A: Peace

SPORTS
Q: What are the three sports in a triathlon?
A: Swimming, bicycling, and running

SCIENCE
Q: Is Polaris located in Antarctica, in space, or inside Earth's crust?
A: In space (Polaris is the North Star.)

• •

SCIENCE
Q: Which of these words is the scientific name for the "windpipe": esophagus, trachea, or larynx?
A: Trachea

SPORTS
Q: What all-American pastime has Abner Doubleday been credited with developing?
A: Baseball

OUR WORLD
Q: Which revered building serves as the spiritual and administrative hub of the Roman Catholic Church?
A: The Vatican

MEDIA
Q: How many foot pedals are on a standard piano: 1, 3, or 5?
A: 3

NATURE
Q: True or false? Male mosquitoes bite.
A: False (only females do)

FAME
Q: What's the nickname for A. A. Milne's Edward Bear?
A: Winnie the Pooh

BLOCK 28

BLOCK 29

FAME
Q: What country legend has a name that makes him sound weary, but made a comeback with his 2000 album, *If Only I Could Fly*?
A: Merle Haggard

NATURE
Q: Turkey's Mount Ararat has traditionally been considered the place where what famous vessel landed?
A: Noah's Ark

MEDIA
Q: Which half of the *Laverne and Shirley* duo became a big-name Hollywood director?
A: Laverne (Penny Marshall)

OUR WORLD
Q: What two Asian countries account for nearly half of the world's population?
A: China and India

SPORTS
Q: The U.S. boycotted the Olympic Games in 1980 to protest the Soviet invasion of what country?
A: Afghanistan

SCIENCE
Q: Who conducted experiments with dogs that led to the idea of a conditioned reflex: Sir Isaac Newton, Jack London, or Ivan Pavlov?
A: Ivan Pavlov

SCIENCE
Q: Earth is surrounded by many "spheres," such as the stratosphere and the exosphere. As a group, what are these regions called?
A: The atmosphere

SPORTS
Q: Deion Sanders played professionally in both baseball and football. What was his best sport in high school?
A: Basketball

OUR WORLD
Q: What Washington mountain erupted in the 1980s, causing ash and debris to drift to neighboring states?
A: Mount St. Helens

MEDIA
Q: How many wicked stepsisters does Cinderella have: one, two, or three?
A: Two

NATURE
Q: What part of the name tyrannosaurus rex means lizard?
A: "Saurus"

FAME
Q: Did Geena Davis play Thelma or Louise?
A: Thelma

BLOCK 30

GAME OF KNOWLEDGE

BLOCK 31

FAME	Q: Liberia honored the fifth U.S. president by naming its capital after him. What is the capital of Liberia? A: Monrovia (After James Monroe)
NATURE	Q: What kind of storm, immortalized in Sebastian Junger's best selling book, sank the *Andrea Gail* in 1991? A: *The Perfect Storm*
MEDIA	Q: Who wrote the run-away bestsellers *A Time to Kill* and *The Pelican Brief*: Scott Turow, John Grisham, or Patricia Highsmith? A: John Grisham
OUR WORLD	Q: Who were the fly-by-night brothers that made airplane history in 1903? A: The Wright brothers
SPORTS	Q: In which of these gymnastic positions is the gymnast's body perfectly straight: layout, pike, or tuck? A: Layout
SCIENCE	Q: In which part of the human body is the cochlea found: the ear, the chest, or the eye? A: The ear

• •

SCIENCE	Q: Was the Hubble Space Telescope launched in 1980, 1990, or 2000? A: 1990
SPORTS	Q: Which of the four major sport leagues (NBA, NFL, NHL, MLB) was the first to "start" a woman? A: The NHL (Manon Rheaume started in a pre-season game for the Tampa Bay Lightning on Sept. 23, 1992)
OUR WORLD	Q: What is the creepy, crawly, and relatively common phobia that was also the title of a 1990s movie? A: Arachnophobia (fear of spiders)
MEDIA	Q: In what century did the "Star Spangled Banner" become the official U.S. national anthem by an act of Congress? A: Twentieth century (1931)
NATURE	Q: True or false? Starfish (also known as seastars) are fish. A: False
FAME	Q: The London Telegraph proclaimed which Victorian author and creator of Ebenezer Scrooge as "The Man Who Invented Christmas"? A: Charles Dickens

BLOCK 32

• • • • • • • • • • • • • • 102 • • • • • • • • • • • • • •

BLOCK 33

FAME
Q: The country where Jim Carrey was born shares the first two letters of his last name. Name the country.
A: Canada

NATURE
Q: Which type of animal has a backbone: an invertebrate or a vertebrate?
A: A vertebrate

MEDIA
Q: What sci-fi television show features commentary from both humans and robots, and is known as "MST3K"?
A: *Mystery Science Theater 3000*

OUR WORLD
Q: How many zeros are in 1 trillion?
A: 12

SPORTS
Q: Bela Karoli is considered the most successful coach in the history of what sport?
A: Women's gymnastics

SCIENCE
Q: Name the vessel invented in 1959 that can hover above smooth surfaces such as water or ice.
A: Hovercraft

- -

SCIENCE
Q: Which of these tiny particles has one unit of positive electricity: an electron, a neutron, or a proton?
A: A proton

SPORTS
Q: The Miami Dolphins beat the Kansas City Chiefs on December 25, 1971. At 82 minutes, 40 seconds, this game holds what NFL record?
A: Longest game

OUR WORLD
Q: Which came first: the American Revolution, the French Revolution, or the Industrial Revolution?
A: The American Revolution

MEDIA
Q: True or false? Barbra Streisand and Katharine Hepburn tied for the Oscar® for Best Actress in a motion picture in 1968.
A: True

NATURE
Q: Branches that symbolize peace appear in an eagle's talons on the back of a U.S.$1 bill. What tree are these branches from?
A: The olive tree

FAME
Q: What TV and movie family includes Morticia, Gomez, and Uncle Fester?
A: *The Addams Family*

BLOCK 34

BLOCK 35

FAME
Q: Who did not listen to John the Baptist: Pharisees, tax collectors, prostitutes, or sinners?
A: Pharisees

NATURE
Q: What kind of horse is carried to term and given birth to by its father?
A: A seahorse (which isn't actually a horse at all, it's a fish!)

MEDIA
Q: While the waiters sing, what slurp-able Italian food do Lady and Tramp share?
A: Spaghetti and meatballs

OUR WORLD
Q: What region of the U.K. sounds like a large aquatic mammal?
A: Wales

SPORTS
Q: True or false? Mike Tyson bit Evander Holyfield's nose during a heavyweight boxing match.
A: False (Tyson bit Holyfield's ear.)

SCIENCE
Q: Which of these did Sir Isaac Newton not devise or discover: calculus, the Law of Universal Gravitation, or the speed of light?
A: The speed of light

- -

SCIENCE
Q: Name three of the five largest human organs.
A: Skin, liver, brain, lungs, and heart

SPORTS
Q: True or false? No NFL quarterback has ever rushed for over 1,000 yards in a season.
A: True

OUR WORLD
Q: Name the three European countries that make up the Benelux.
A: Belgium, The Netherlands, Luxembourg

MEDIA
Q: "Do" and "re" are the first two musical notes. What is the fifth?
A: "So"

NATURE
Q: The name for baby partridges (and baby quail) makes a lot of sense. What is it?
A: Cheeper

FAME
Q: What Latin heartthrob shook his "Bon Bon" in 2000?
A: Ricky Martin

BLOCK 36

BLOCK 37

FAME
Q: Is Pope John Paul II Austrian, Polish, or Romanian?
A: Polish

NATURE
Q: In 1988, which of the then Soviet Republics was devastated by an earthquake measuring 8.3 on the Richter Scale?
A: Armenia

MEDIA
Q: Which of these composers lived first: Johann Sebastian Bach, Johannes Brahms, or Ludwig van Beethoven?
A: Johannes Brahms

OUR WORLD
Q: How many days longer than a week does Hanukkah last?
A: One (Hanukkah lasts eight days.)

SPORTS
Q: Kathy Whitworth is a hall of famer with 88 victories to her credit in what sport?
A: Women's golf

SCIENCE
Q: Do neutrons have a positive, negative, or neutral charge?
A: Neutral

• •

SCIENCE
Q: True or false? Hot air balloons float because hot air is lighter than cold air.
A: True

SPORTS
Q: After the death of her husband and skating partner in 1995, which Russian doubles Olympic gold medallist went on to perform as a soloist?
A: Ekaterina Gordeeva

OUR WORLD
Q: Which European car company owns Bentley and Lamborghini?
A: Volkswagen

MEDIA
Q: What type of poem has five lines and shares its name with an Irish county?
A: Limerick

NATURE
Q: Which of these trees is coniferous: fir, oak, maple, or all three?
A: Fir

FAME
Q: Name two twentieth century U.S. presidents whose last names begin with the letter "C."
A: Calvin Coolidge, Jimmy Carter, or Bill Clinton

BLOCK 38

BLOCK 1

FAME
Q: Name the politician who made peanuts before collecting a presidential paycheck.
A: Jimmy Carter

NATURE
Q: Name one of the main islands in the Mediterranean Sea.
A: Majorca, Corsica, Sardinia, Sicily, Crete, Cyprus, or Rhodes

MEDIA
Q: Name two of the five kids who got a golden ticket in *Willie Wonka and the Chocolate Factory*?
A: Charlie Bucket, Augustus Gloop, Veruca Salt, Violet Beauregarde, Mike Teavee

OUR WORLD
Q: What civilization built Machu Picchu, a city in the Andes mountains of Peru that was rediscovered in 1911?
A: The Incan civilization

SPORTS
Q: What baseball player once said, "If it wasn't for baseball, I'd be in either the penitentiary or the cemetery."?
A: Babe Ruth

SCIENCE
Q: If you're highly stressed, you may suffer from hypertension. What's the common term for this condition?
A: High blood pressure

• •

SCIENCE
Q: Which element is the lightest and is likely to give you a lift: oxygen, helium, or nitrogen?
A: Helium

SPORTS
Q: In what year was the first Super Bowl held: 1954, 1961, or 1967?
A: 1967

OUR WORLD
Q: What Asian city has "soul" and was the host of the Olympic games in 1988?
A: Seoul, South Korea

MEDIA
Q: What Irish author courted critics and readers alike with his moving memoir, *Angela's Ashes*?
A: Frank McCourt

NATURE
Q: What type of bird is the yellow-bellied sapsucker: a lark, a sparrow, or a woodpecker?
A: A woodpecker

FAME
Q: What late night personality has a gap-toothed grin and really knows his Top Ten Lists?
A: David Letterman

BLOCK 2

BLOCK 3

FAME
Q: Who is the only woman to have attended three U.S. Inaugural Balls as First Lady?
A: Eleanor Roosevelt

NATURE
Q: True or false? You can be stung by a dead jellyfish.
A: True

MEDIA
Q: What Disney character wears a sailor suit?
A: Donald Duck

OUR WORLD
Q: What Canadian province's name is the Latin version of "New Scotland"?
A: Nova Scotia

SPORTS
Q: In the 1994-95 season, Jason Kidd and Grant Hill tied for Rookie of the Year in what professional sport?
A: Basketball

SCIENCE
Q: Some types of fuel were formed millions of years ago from decomposed plant and animal matter. What are those fuels called?
A: Fossil fuels

· ·

SCIENCE
Q: What sturdy synthetic fiber did Wallace Carothers create in 1934 that gave Dupont a leg up on the competition?
A: Nylon

SPORTS
Q: When a soccer player scores a point against his/her own team, what is it called?
A: An own goal

OUR WORLD
Q: What ingredient in beer might put a skip in your step and a bitter taste in your mouth?
A: Hops

MEDIA
Q: What comedian carved a niche for himself as the Church Lady on *Saturday Night Live?*
A: Dana Carvey

NATURE
Q: What ocean has one of Southern Asia's most densely populated countries as its namesake?
A: The Indian Ocean

FAME
Q: What god of wine and ecstasy did the Romans celebrate in an annual festival until 186 B.C.—when the party got out of hand?
A: Bacchus

BLOCK 4

BLOCK 5

FAME	Q: What young boy has had a 50-year career and is often called a Good Man? A: Charlie Brown
NATURE	Q: What does an octopus do with its ink: change its color, poison its prey, or form a cloud that it can hide behind? A: Form a cloud
MEDIA	Q: What was jazz saxophonist Charlie Parker's fine-feathered nickname? A: Bird
OUR WORLD	Q: How's it going? My name's Robert, but you can call me…What are the three most common American nicknames for Robert? A: Rob, Bob, and Bobby
SPORTS	Q: In 1964, Willie Mays was the first African American player to receive what team distinction? A: Team Captain (San Francisco Giants)
SCIENCE	Q: Which of these elements burns with a blue flame and gives off a smell like rotten eggs: magnesium, carbon, or sulfur? A: Sulfur

• •

SCIENCE	Q: The Soviet launch of Sputnik started the Space Race. During which decade was Sputnik launched? A: The 1950s (1957)
SPORTS	Q: In 1823, what rugged team sport was invented that let players carry the ball (instead of just kicking it)? A: Rugby
OUR WORLD	Q: According to official Vatican sources, what was the first date of the twenty-first century? A: January 1, 2001
MEDIA	Q: Who was the boyish sister in *Little Women* who cut her hair short to the dismay of her family? A: Jo
NATURE	Q: What suspension bridge sits only eight miles from the epicenter of its city's most devastating earthquake? A: The Golden Gate Bridge
FAME	Q: What royal-sounding bandleader and composer used his solid musical base to attract the top jazz musicians of his day? A: Count Basie

BLOCK 6

BLOCK 7

FAME
Q: What famous moose is constantly spoiling Boris Badinoff's evil plans?
A: Bullwinkle

NATURE
Q: Name the sea urchin that burrows into sand for protection, and shares its name with a unit of currency.
A: Sand dollar

MEDIA
Q: What *Jungle Book* bear was a pal to Mowgli and has a name that sounds like a color?
A: Baloo

OUR WORLD
Q: What continent in the Western Hemisphere contains the countries that signed NAFTA?
A: North America (North American Free Trade Agreement)

SPORTS
Q: Since 1936, Olympic javelin competitions have only been won by athletes from which two Scandinavian countries?
A: Finland and Sweden

SCIENCE
Q: Of the 94 naturally occurring chemical elements, are the majority solid, liquid, or gas?
A: Solid

• •

SCIENCE
Q: What did physicist Robert Oppenheimer witness on July 16, 1945 in the New Mexico desert that prompted him to say, "We knew the world would not be the same"?
A: The first explosion of an atomic bomb

SPORTS
Q: What ritzy eastern seaboard city is home to the Tennis Hall of Fame?
A: Newport, Rhode Island

OUR WORLD
Q: What state has four i's but can't see?
A: Mississippi

MEDIA
Q: Which dim-witted *Friend* shares his name with a baby kangaroo and uses the pick-up line, "How you doin'?"
A: Joey

NATURE
Q: What larger relative of a chive sounds like it needs a plumber?
A: A leek

FAME
Q: Staunch conservative Arnold Schwarzenegger entered what Democratic political dynasty when he married Maria Shriver?
A: The Kennedy family

BLOCK 8

BLOCK 9

FAME
Q: What teen pop sensation got her start on *The Mickey Mouse Club* and topped the charts in 2000 with "Oops … I Did it Again"?
A: Britney Spears

NATURE
Q: What land mammal has skin that can weigh up to 2,000 pounds?
A: The elephant

MEDIA
Q: What's the uplifting title of the classic Christmas movie about a man named George Bailey?
A: *It's a Wonderful Life*

OUR WORLD
Q: What central European country separated peacefully into two new nations in 1993?
A: Czechoslovakia

SPORTS
Q: True or false? Hockey's Stanley Cup has the name of seven women on it.
A: True

SCIENCE
Q: In general, which of these forces is weakest: nuclear, electromagnetic, or gravitational?
A: Gravitational

• •

SCIENCE
Q: Which blood type is a "universal donor": A, AB, or O?
A: O

SPORTS
Q: What position did basketball superstar Bill Russell play: center, power forward, or guard?
A: Center

OUR WORLD
Q: Who were the class of military governors who ruled Japan until the mid-1800s?
A: The Shoguns

MEDIA
Q: How many years of solitude are in the title of a novel by Nobel Prize-winner Gabriel García-Márquez?
A: 100 (*One Hundred Years of Solitude*)

NATURE
Q: What gas traps Earth's heat and may cause the greenhouse effect?
A: Carbon dioxide

FAME
Q: Name the Greek god of the Sun who shares his name with a NASA space program.
A: Apollo

BLOCK 10

BLOCK 11

FAME
Q: Was painter Claude Monet a realist, cubist, or an impressionist?
A: Impressionist

NATURE
Q: Nevada's Hoover Dam provides what important service?
A: Hydroelectric power

MEDIA
Q: What color is Nickelodeon's logo?
A: Orange

OUR WORLD
Q: Which of these New York islands held a processing station for immigrants from the 1890s to the 1950s: Ellis Island, Liberty Island, or Staten Island?
A: Ellis Island

SPORTS
Q: WWF is the abbreviated term for what popular sporting association?
A: World Wrestling Federation

SCIENCE
Q: What object did Benjamin Franklin invent after his famous experiment with a kite, a key, and lightning?
A: The lightning rod

• •

SCIENCE
Q: Which of these chemicals released by the body causes allergic symptoms in people with hay fever: antigen, leukotriene, or histamine?
A: Histamine

SPORTS
Q: In auto racing, what critical car components are sometimes "staggering"?
A: The tires (Staggering means the tires are bigger on one side of the car than the other.)

OUR WORLD
Q: Name the common fruit that has no single word in English that rhymes with it.
A: Orange

MEDIA
Q: What 1978 holiday flick were viewers treated to that featured a knife-wielding killer named Michael Myers?
A: Halloween

NATURE
Q: The male of what type of white bird shares its name with the core of an ear of corn?
A: The swan (cob)

FAME
Q: Who was not an original member of The Who: Pete Townsend, John Bonham, or Keith Moon?
A: John Bonham

BLOCK 12

BLOCK 13

FAME
Q: According to the Bible, what tower gave rise to the creation of different languages?
A: The Tower of Babel

NATURE
Q: Which sweet-smelling flora shares its name with a character from Disney's *Aladdin*?
A: Jasmine

MEDIA
Q: Samuel Clemens penned *The Adventures of Tom Sawyer*. What is Clemens' pen name?
A: Mark Twain

OUR WORLD
Q: What great city, now called Istanbul, was founded by Constantine the Great in 330 A.D.?
A: Constantinople

SPORTS
Q: What intimidating Dodger pitcher was 6'5" and was known for hitting a batter with the ball an alarming average of once nearly every 22 innings?
A: Don Drysdale

SCIENCE
Q: True or false? Most scientists believe that the universe is contracting.
A: False (It's rapidly expanding.)

• •

SCIENCE
A: True
Q: True or false? Objects in motion remain in motion unless acted upon by an external force.

SPORTS
A: The New Jersey Nets
Q: The number one NBA draft pick for 2000, Kenyon Martin, went to what "new" team?

OUR WORLD
A: England
Q: The first postage stamp was used during the Victorian era in what country?

MEDIA
A: Annie (Oakley)
Q: In his 1964 musical, who did Irving Berlin tell to "Get Your Gun"?

NATURE
A: The Chesapeake
Q: Which bay borders Virginia and Maryland and is the largest Atlantic Ocean inlet in the eastern United States?

FAME
A: False
Q: True or false? Oliver Stone is Sharon Stone's uncle.

BLOCK 14

BLOCK 15

FAME
Q: Four U.S. presidents have been assassinated. Name three of them.
A: Abraham Lincoln, James Garfield, William McKinley, and John F. Kennedy

NATURE
Q: Do 17-year locusts appear once every 17 years, or live for 17 years once they appear?
A: Appear every 17 years

MEDIA
Q: Is Ren, of *Ren and Stimpy*, a cat, a dog, or a mouse?
A: A dog

OUR WORLD
Q: What year did the Japanese bomb Pearl Harbor?
A: 1941

SPORTS
Q: Name the three Opens and the one regal British event in professional tennis that make up the Grand Slam.
A: The French Open, United States Open, Australian Open, and Wimbledon

SCIENCE
Q: The first steam locomotive reached a top speed of 5 mph. During which century did it first chug along?
A: Nineteenth century (1804)

• •

SCIENCE
Q: Ursa Major contains seven stars that form a pattern particularly appropriate for the Milky Way. What is this formation known as?
A: The Big Dipper

SPORTS
Q: What did the Dodgers do to the Yankees in 1955, 1963, and 1981?
A: Beat them in the World Series

OUR WORLD
Q: What swanky region of France borders the Mediterranean Sea and is host to a major film festival each year?
A: The Riviera (Cannes)

MEDIA
Q: Which superhero is also known as The Caped Crusader?
A: Batman

NATURE
Q: What type of water formation do you usually find near an oxbow lake?
A: A river or stream

FAME
Q: Investitures bestow what high honor on British individuals for their achievements?
A: Knighthood

BLOCK 16

BLOCK 17

FAME
Q: What famous Van shares his last name with a Door?
A: Van Morrison

NATURE
Q: Which of these animals' young are not called cubs: bear, fox, or wolf?
A: Wolf (Their young are called pups.)

MEDIA
Q: The mice Bianca and Bernard are the saving grace in what 1977 Disney animated classic?
A: *The Rescuers*

OUR WORLD
Q: What country made headlines with the election of Vicente Fox Quesada as its new president in 2000?
A: Mexico

SPORTS
Q: True or false? Germany and Japan were not invited to participate in the 1948 Olympics in London.
A: True

SCIENCE
Q: True or false? A vaccine is made of dead or weakened germs from the disease it's used to fight.
A: True

• •

SCIENCE
Q: Which heavenly body is farther away from Earth: the moon or the sun?
A: The sun

SPORTS
Q: NBA superstar Patrick Ewing was not born in the U.S. On what island nation was he born?
A: Jamaica

OUR WORLD
Q: What eastern country, home to karaoke and Asahi beer, has the highest life expectancy rate for females?
A: Japan

MEDIA
Q: Which U.S. metropolis has newspapers that sell more copies each day than any other U.S. city?
A: New York

NATURE
Q: What natural phenomenon causes thunder?
A: Lightning

FAME
Q: What exclusive public school did Prince William enter in 1996?
A: Eton College

BLOCK 18

BLOCK 19

FAME
Q: Pre-Communist Russia had two "Great" rulers—one male and one female. Name one of these rulers.
A: Peter (I) the Great, Catherine (II) the Great

NATURE
Q: What sea with a compass direction in its name lies between England and Norway?
A: The North Sea

MEDIA
Q: What are the last names of the famous singers David, Stephen, Graham, and Neil?
A: Crosby, Stills, Nash, and Young

OUR WORLD
Q: In what Asian country did demonstrations in Tiananmen Square lead to violence?
A: China

SPORTS
Q: American football traces its origins from two sports. What are they?
A: Rugby and soccer

SCIENCE
Q: When liquids evaporate, what physical state of matter do they become?
A: Gases

• •

SCIENCE
Q: Many metals and alloys become superconductors at low temperatures. What do they conduct?
A: Electrical current (electricity)

SPORTS
Q: Who is the official timekeeper in a soccer game?
A: The referee

OUR WORLD
Q: Francis Drake was the first Englishman to sail around the world. What title was added to his name upon his return?
A: Sir (Knight)

MEDIA
Q: In Dr. Seuss' How the Grinch Stole Christmas, who lives in Who-ville?
A: The Whos (including Cindy-Lou)

NATURE
Q: Is a group of kangaroos called a swarm, a troop, or a mob?
A: A mob

FAME
Q: NBA star Michael Jordan retired in 1993 to follow a lifelong (but short-lived) dream to play what?
A: Baseball

BLOCK 20

BLOCK 21

FAME
Q: What young Biblical figure took on a giant named Goliath?
A: David

NATURE
Q: Name one of the three colors—other than white—that can be typically found in an iceberg.
A: Brown, black, green (They are colored by sediment and plankton deposits)

MEDIA
Q: Which 1980s nighttime soap was set on a sprawling winery in California's Napa Valley: *Dynasty*, *Falcon Crest*, or *Knot's Landing*?
A: *Falcon Crest*

OUR WORLD
Q: What kind of meat adorns more pizzas in the U.S. than any other topping?
A: Pepperoni

SPORTS
Q: In 1994, the U.S. Figure Skating Association banned which skater for life?
A: Tonya Harding

SCIENCE
Q: Which Wright brother was in the biplane for the historic first flight at Kitty Hawk, NC in 1903?
A: Orville

SCIENCE
Q: True or false? The left side of your brain controls the left side of your body.
A: False (The left side of your brain controls the right side of your body.)

SPORTS
Q: In auto racing, what does a white flag indicate?
A: Leaders are starting their final lap.

OUR WORLD
Q: Is "Be prepared" the motto of the Girl Scouts, the Boy Scouts, or high school sex educators?
A: Boy Scouts

MEDIA
Q: How many stooges did The Three Stooges feature in all: three, four, or six?
A: Six (Moe, Larry, Curly, Shemp, Joe, and Curly Joe)

NATURE
Q: Which part of the cinnamon tree is the spice made from: the bark, the fruit, or the leaves?
A: The bark

FAME
Q: Name the "Beverly Hills Ninja" and onetime *Saturday Night Live* regular who died tragically in 1997.
A: Chris Farley

BLOCK 22

BLOCK 23

FAME
Q: Who assassinated Senator Robert Kennedy in 1968: Sadham Hussein, Sirhan Sirhan, or Lee Harvey Oswald?
A: Sirhan Sirhan

NATURE
Q: True or false? The majority of the animals on Earth have a backbone.
A: False (roughly 95% do not)

MEDIA
Q: What Helen Fielding novel chronicles the life of a neurotic single woman in her thirties and was made into a 2001 film starring Renee Zellweger?
A: *Bridget Jones's Diary*

OUR WORLD
Q: Byeli means white in Russian. Name the country of "White Russia."
A: Belarus

SPORTS
Q: What two U.S. figure skaters finished with gold and silver in the 1998 Olympics in Nagano, Japan?
A: Tara Lipinski (gold) and Michelle Kwan (silver)

SCIENCE
Q: What does NASA stand for?
A: National Aeronautics and Space Administration

• •

SCIENCE
Q: A penny for your thoughts: What common metal goes into making both brass and bronze?
A: Copper

SPORTS
Q: What is the artificial bait used to attract fish called?
A: Lure

OUR WORLD
Q: What "jaded" country has a long coastline and shares its name with a color.
A: Greenland

MEDIA
Q: What famous crooner dreamed of a "White Christmas"?
A: Bing Crosby

NATURE
Q: True or false? About 50% of the eggs a sea turtle lays reach adulthood.
A: False (Only about 1% survive.)

FAME
Q: What color was the Teletubbie that Reverend Jerry Falwell found offensive?
A: Purple

BLOCK 24

BLOCK 25

FAME
Q: What mythological character sounds like a geography buff and carries the weight of the world on his shoulders?
A: Atlas

NATURE
Q: In total, which produces more carbon monoxide: factory smoke or automobile exhaust?
A: Automobile exhaust

MEDIA
Q: What is the name of Sgt. Pepper's group?
A: Lonely Hearts Club Band

OUR WORLD
Q: Which Soviet leader commanded the USSR during World War II and has a last name that means steel in Russian?
A: Joseph Stalin

SPORTS
Q: What brave hitter played for 23 seasons in the major leagues and broke Babe Ruth's career home-run record in 1974?
A: Hank Aaron

SCIENCE
Q: Are the triceps located in the arms, the legs, or the back?
A: The arms

• •

SCIENCE
Q: Would rubber, copper, or plastic generally be the best conductor of electricity?
A: Copper

SPORTS
Q: Archie Griffin is the only football player to win what twice, in 1974 and 1975?
A: The Heisman Trophy

OUR WORLD
Q: Name the elusive islands located at the southern tip of Alaska.
A: The Aleutian Islands

MEDIA
Q: Which TV personality pleaded, "Please, don't squeeze the Charmin!": Mr. Whipple, Chuck Charmin, or Tidy Tim?
A: Mr. Whipple

NATURE
Q: Hippos, elephants, and rhinos are pachyderms. Does pachyderm mean: giant animal, thick-skinned animal, or wild animal?
A: Thick-skinned animal

FAME
Q: Which actor mastered *The Matrix* and fronts the band Dogstar?
A: Keanu Reeves

BLOCK 26

BLOCK 27

FAME
Q: What actor won a Best Actor Oscar® for his stellar performance in *American Beauty*?
A: Kevin Spacey

NATURE
Q: What part of the pea plant are the peas?
A: The seeds

MEDIA
Q: What was Cameron Diaz's first movie: *The Mask*, *There's Something about Mary*, or *Dumb and Dumber*?
A: *The Mask*

OUR WORLD
Q: The 2,400 mile long St. Lawrence River is located between two countries in the Western Hemisphere. Name one of them.
A: Canada, U.S.

SPORTS
Q: In 1940, who was born Lee Jun Fan in San Francisco's Chinatown?
A: Bruce Lee

SCIENCE
Q: Radar can determine an object's distance and the direction it is traveling. What else is radar primarily used to determine?
A: An object's speed

SCIENCE
Q: What twentieth century astronomer made important contributions to the study of galaxies and had an important space telescope named after him in 1990?
A: Edwin Hubble

SPORTS
Q: In baseball, does a curveball really curve?
A: Yes

OUR WORLD
Q: Name the party that took place in a New England harbor in the 1700s.
A: The Boston Tea Party

MEDIA
Q: What 1952 classic J. R. R. Tolkien novel features the character Bilbo Baggins?
A: *The Hobbit*

NATURE
Q: In 1902, the entire bustling town of St. Pierre, Martinique—except for a lucky fellow who was incarcerated in an underground cell—was incinerated by what?
A: A volcano (Mont Pelee erupted.)

FAME
Q: Ben and Jerry's Ice Cream was founded in 1978 in a renovated gas station in what New England state?
A: Vermont

BLOCK 28

GAME OF KNOWLEDGE

BLOCK 29

FAME
Q: Who is considered the "Godfather of Grunge": Neil Young or Kurt Cobain?
A: Neil Young

NATURE
Q: Which continent has the least rainfall?
A: Antarctica

MEDIA
Q: Who made the violin that sold for the highest price ever (over $1.2 million): Mozart, Copernicus, or Stradivarius?
A: Stradivarius

OUR WORLD
Q: China's Ming dynasty ruled for more than 250 years. During which century did it fall: the tenth, the seventeenth, or the nineteenth?
A: The seventeenth century (1644)

SPORTS
Q: What is star running back Walter Payton's sugarcoated nickname?
A: Sweetness

SCIENCE
Q: True or false? The imprints or hardened remains of plants and animals are called sediment.
A: False (They're called fossils.)

SCIENCE
Q: What unit of length is equal to the distance that light travels in a vacuum in one year?
A: One light-year

SPORTS
Q: With more than a dozen career Grand Slam titles, which player has more titles than any other man in tennis?
A: Pete Sampras

OUR WORLD
Q: Which sunny state borders the Pacific and has one of the U.S.'s largest prison populations?
A: California

MEDIA
Q: What song did Elton John contribute to *The Lion King* soundtrack: "I Just Can't Wait to be King," "Hakuna Matata," or "Circle of Life"?
A: "Circle of Life"

NATURE
Q: Which living animal has a genetic make-up that is most similar to that of humans?
A: The chimpanzee

FAME
Q: What indie actress was named after supermodel Suzy Parker and starred in the 2000 spoof *Best in Show?*
A: Parker Posey

BLOCK 30

121

BLOCK 31

FAME
Q: Imelda Marcos, wife of former Philippine President Ferdinand Marcos, owned 3,000 pairs of something. What were they?
A: Shoes

NATURE
Q: What is the name of the mountain range that extends from Newfoundland, Canada all the way down to the state of Alabama?
A: The Appalachians

MEDIA
Q: True or false? The author of the novel *Frankenstein* was a woman.
A: True (Mary Shelley)

OUR WORLD
Q: The main ingredient in Coca-Cola® isn't sugar. What is it?
A: Carbonated water

SPORTS
Q: Which San Francisco 49er holds the NFL's highest career passing rating: Steve Young or Joe Montana?
A: Steve Young (Montana is second)

SCIENCE
Q: Listen closely: a long string and a short string are plucked. Which string produces the sound with the higher pitch?
A: The short string

• •

SCIENCE
Q: Which of these sets of sex chromosomes produces a female child: XX, XY or YY?
A: XX

SPORTS
Q: In the first election to the Baseball Hall of Fame, in 1936, which controversial player received the most votes?
A: Ty Cobb

OUR WORLD
Q: During the 1990 Persian Gulf War, what country fought the coalition of Arab and Western nations?
A: Iraq

MEDIA
Q: What were the four herbs that Simon & Garfunkel sang about in the song "Scarborough Fair?"
A: Parsley, sage, rosemary, thyme

NATURE
Q: Which edible grassy plant that contains 14 of the 16 essential minerals shares its name with a Little Rascal?
A: Alfalfa

FAME
Q: Name the 1965 classic film concerning a Russian doctor with the Russian Revolution as a backdrop.
A: *Doctor Zhivago*

BLOCK 32

BLOCK 33

FAME
Q: What actor was the "king of the world" and has something in common with da Vinci?
A: Leonardo Dicaprio

NATURE
Q: True or false? Boll weevils attack sugar cane.
A: False (They attack cotton.)

MEDIA
Q: What is "the question" in Shakespeare's *Hamlet*?
A: "To be or not to be?"

OUR WORLD
Q: Name the only South American country that borders the Pacific Ocean and the Caribbean Sea.
A: Columbia

SPORTS
Q: True or false? A Canadian invented basketball.
A: True

SCIENCE
Q: During which decade were the first seven U.S. astronauts chosen?
A: The 1950s

• •

SCIENCE
A: True
Q: True or false? Magnets can only pick up objects with metal in them.

SPORTS
A: Las Vegas and Reno, Nevada
Q: The only two college teams you can't wager on in Las Vegas are from what two betting cities?

OUR WORLD
A: *The Monitor*
Q: What well-known ironclad vessel shares its name with a large Australian lizard?

MEDIA
A: Saturday night
Q: On average, which night of the week has the fewest prime time TV viewers?

NATURE
A: The blue whale
Q: What colorful mammal is the largest living animal on Earth?

FAME
A: Walt Disney
Q: What Hollywood producer put a duck in a sailor suit—and has won more than 50 Academy Awards?

BLOCK 34

BLOCK 35

FAME
Q: What actress showed off more than her talent and took home a 2001 Oscar® for her role as a real-life single mom fighting a corporate cover-up?
A: Julia Roberts

NATURE
Q: Name two of the nine European countries the Danube River passes through on its way to the Black Sea.
A: Germany, Austria, Slovakia, Hungary, Croatia, Yugoslavia, Bulgaria, Romania, and Moldova.

MEDIA
Q: In which Rocky film did Rocky Balboa take on Mr. T?
A: *Rocky III*

OUR WORLD
Q: Which two oceans does the Panama Canal connect?
A: The Atlantic and the Pacific

SPORTS
Q: In a relay team, what do the runners exchange?
A: A baton

SCIENCE
Q: Which two types of remains become fossil fuels over time: animal, plant, or mineral?
A: Animal and plant remains

• •

SCIENCE
Q: True or false? A flower cannot make seeds unless it has been pollinated.
A: True

SPORTS
Q: The short-lived USFL lasted for how many seasons: three, four, or five?
A: Three

OUR WORLD
Q: What Egyptian astronomer set forth the long-believed theory that the Earth was the center of the universe: Ptolemy, Qerti, or Copernicus?
A: Ptolemy

MEDIA
Q: "Redrum" is murder spelled backwards. Which prolific author made Redrum famous?
A: Stephen King (In *The Shining*)

NATURE
Q: What wise bird of prey asks the same question over and over again?
A: The owl

FAME
Q: Who was Abraham Lincoln's successor—and the first president to be impeached?
A: Andrew Johnson

BLOCK 36

BLOCK 37

FAME
Q: Name the character that can fly, but isn't a bird, and will never grow up.
A: Peter Pan

NATURE
Q: Acorns come from what tree?
A: The oak tree

MEDIA
Q: Which instrument has more strings: the guitar or the banjo?
A: The guitar (6 strings)

OUR WORLD
Q: True or false? The Soviet Union was a U.S. ally during World War II.
A: True

SPORTS
Q: In which genteel sport would you encounter a bunker?
A: Golf

SCIENCE
Q: True or false? Human beings have 15 vertebrae.
A: False (The average human has 33.)

● ●

SCIENCE
Q: Which of these planets is closest to the sun: Jupiter, Uranus, or Neptune?
A: Jupiter

SPORTS
Q: How many times has the World Series been canceled?
A: Twice (1904 and 1994)

OUR WORLD
Q: What is the most common street sign along America's highways and byways?
A: Stop sign

MEDIA
Q: Irving Berlin wrote the song "God Bless America." In what country was Berlin born?
A: Russia

NATURE
Q: True or false? Kangaroos hunt and eat other animals.
A: False (They only eat plants.)

FAME
Q: What U.S. president has both a state and a city named after him?
A: George Washington

BLOCK 38

About the Author

Always ahead of the game, Bob Moog's newest undertaking is truly novel. As a game inventor, his credits include such favorites as Twenty Questions® and 30 Second Mysteries®. As the CEO of University Games, he has propelled the company he founded with his college pal into an international operation that now boasts five divisions and over 350 products. Whether hosting his radio show "Games People Play," advising MBA candidates, or inventing games, Bob sees work as serious fun. He now brings his flair for fun and learning to the bookshelf with the Spinner Book line.

Enjoy Spinner Books?

Get an original game!

Find these games and more at

 or your nearest toy store.

UNIVERSITY GAMES

2030 Harrison Street, San Francisco, CA 94110, 1-800-347-4818, www.ugames.com